ROBIN M. HOCHSTRASSER was born in Edinburgh, Scotland. He received his Ph.D. from Edinburgh University in 1955; the author was a member of the chemistry staff at the University of British Columbia until 1963.

Dr. Hochstrasser is the author of numerous articles on the molecular spectroscopy of organic materials. The author is presently associate professor of chemistry at the University of Pennsylvania.

Behavior of Electrons in Atoms

THE GENERAL CHEMISTRY MONOGRAPH SERIES

Russell Johnsen, Editor
Florida State University

Gordon M. Barrow (*Case Institute of Technology*)	THE STRUCTURE OF MOLECULES
Werner Herz (*Florida State University*)	THE SHAPE OF CARBON COMPOUNDS
Edward L. King (*University of Colorado*)	HOW CHEMICAL REACTIONS OCCUR
Bruce H. Mahan (*University of California, Berkeley*)	ELEMENTARY CHEMICAL THERMODYNAMICS
Gregory R. Choppin (*Florida State University*)	NUCLEI AND RADIOACTIVITY
Robin M. Hochstrasser (*University of Pennsylvania*)	BEHAVIOR OF ELECTRONS IN ATOMS

Behavior of Electrons in Atoms

Structure, Spectra, and Photochemistry of Atoms

Robin M. Hochstrasser
University of Pennsylvania

1964
W. A. BENJAMIN, INC. New York Amsterdam

BEHAVIOR OF ELECTRONS IN ATOMS:
Structure, Spectra, and Photochemistry of Atoms

Library of Congress Catalog Card Number 64–21227
Manufactured in the United States of America

The manuscript was put into production on December 16, 1963; this volume was published on May 15, 1964

The publisher is pleased to acknowledge the assistance of Felix Cooper, who produced the illustrations

W. A. BENJAMIN, INC.
New York, New York

Editor's Foreword

THE TEACHING OF GENERAL CHEMISTRY to beginning students becomes each day a more challenging and rewarding task as subject matter becomes more diverse and more complex and as the high school preparation of the student improves. These challenges have evoked a number of responses; this series of monographs for general chemistry is one such response. It is an experiment in the teaching of chemistry which recognizes a number of the problems that plague those who select textbooks and teach chemistry. First, it recognizes that no single book can physically encompass all the various aspects of chemistry that all instructors collectively deem important. Second, it recognizes that no single author is capable of writing authoritatively on *all* the topics that are included in everybody's list of what constitutes general chemistry. Finally, it recognizes the instructor's right to choose those topics that he considers to be important without having to apologize for having omitted large parts of an extensive textbook.

This volume, then, is one of approximately fifteen in the General Chemistry Monograph Series, each written by one or more highly qualified persons very familiar with the current status of the subject by virtue of research in it and also conversant with the problems associated with teaching the subject matter to beginning students. Each volume deals broadly with one of the subdivisions of general chemistry and constitutes a complete entity, far more comprehensive in its coverage than is permitted by the limitation of the standard one-volume text. Taken together, these volumes provide a range of topics from which the individual instructor can easily select those that will provide for his class an appropriate coverage of the material he considers most important.

Furthermore, inclusion of a number of topics that have only recently been considered for general chemistry courses, such as thermodynamics, molecular spectroscopy, and biochemistry, is planned, and these volumes will soon be available. In every instance a modern structural point of view has been adopted with the emphasis on general principles and unifying theory.

These volumes will have other uses also: selected monographs can be used to enrich the more conventional course of study by providing readily available, inexpensive supplements to standard texts. They should also prove valuable to students in other areas of the physical and biological sciences needing supplementary information in any field of chemistry pertinent to their own special interests. Thus, students of biology will find the monographs on biochemistry, organic chemistry, and reaction kinetics particularly useful. Beginning students in physics and meteorology will find the monograph on thermodynamics rewarding. Teachers of elementary science will also find these volumes invaluable aids to bringing them up to date in the various branches of chemistry.

Each monograph has several features which make it especially useful as an aid to teaching. These include a large number of solved examples and problems for the student, a glossary of technical terms, and copious illustrations.

The authors of the several monographs deserve much credit for their enthusiasm which made this experiment possible. Professor Rolfe Herber of Rutgers University has been of invaluable assistance in the preparation of this series, having supplied editorial comment and numerous valuable suggestions on each volume. Thanks are also due to Professor M. Kasha of the Florida State University for many suggestions during the planning stages and for reading several of the manuscripts.

RUSSELL JOHNSEN

Tallahassee, Florida
October 1962

Preface

THIS BRIEF MONOGRAPH deals with the elementary basis of the electronic structure of atoms. The present treatment is far from complete primarily because of the omission of the mathematical framework for the quantum ideas. Even without this framework a beginning student of science should easily manage to glean the fundamental concepts of quantum theory through their relation to the spectra and experimental electronic structure of atoms. This task is facilitated by a close study of the very experiments that provided the original theoretical stimulus.

Accordingly, the framework of this monograph is experimental rather than theoretical. The nature of electromagnetic radiation and the early atomic spectral results are contained in Chapter I. Chapter II deals with the interactions between atoms and electrons, and particularly stresses the Franck-Hertz experiments. Chapters III and IV treat the wavenature of particles, qualitative quantum theory leading to the Pauli Principle, and the orbital and shell structure of atoms. A brief treatment of the nomenclature of atomic spectra, and its physical basis, is given in Chapter V. Chapters VI and VII introduce some dynamic aspects of atomic systems, and special emphasis given to the mechanisms and experimental manifestations of electronic energy transfer and storage. The Zeeman effect is given a brief treatment in Chapter VIII. The last chapter bridges some of the narrower gaps between atomic and molecular systems as evidenced by spectroscopy.

The subject matter is intended to be understandable by beginning students in science, although much of the material in Chapters II, V, VII, VIII, and IX has not normally been treated in elementary texts. I think that young students deserve an early introduction to some of the exciting experimental advances which have led to our current understanding of the structure of matter, and that is why the monograph was written.

I acknowledge, with thanks, helpful comments by Dr. J. N. Butler and Dr. A. V. Bree. Dr. A. Adler helped considerably with the proofreading, and Carol Hochstrasser helped with other details.

Robin M. Hochstrasser

Philadelphia, Pennsylvania
March 1964

. . . . Ah where are they going?
And where have they been?
Ask the lanterns that swing in the sky.

Contents

Editor's Foreword v

Preface vii

I Atomic Spectra 1

1–1 Elementary Principles 2
1–2 Experimental Spectroscopy 7
1–3 Series Relations for Spectral Lines 12
1–4 Summary 15
Problems 17

II The Interactions between Atoms and Electrons 18

2–1 Electrons and Electron Energies 18
2–2 The Bohr Atom 22
2–3 Electron-Atom-Collision Experiments 25
2–4 The Excitation of Spectral Lines by Electronic Collisions 28
2–5 Continuous Atomic Spectra 30
2–6 Summary 33

III Quantum Theory of Atomic Structure 35

3–1 The Diffraction of Waves 35
3–2 Angular Momentum 37
3–3 The Quantum Mechanics 38
3–4 The Wave Representation of the Electron 40

3–5 The Statistical Basis of Knowledge 41
3–6 Results from the Wave Mechanical Theory of the Electron 43
3–7 Atomic Orbitals 48
3–8 Electron Spin 54
3–9 Summary 56

IV The Pauli Principle and the Electronic Structure of Atoms 58

4–1 The Occupation of Atomic Orbitals by Electrons 58
4–2 The Electronic Structure of Atoms and the Periodic Table 65
4–3 The Stability of Filled and Half-Filled Subshells 68
4–4 Some Chemical Uses of the Periodic Table 76
Problems 77

V Energy Terms and States of Atoms 78

5–1 A More Formal Description of the Energy of an Atom 78
5–2 Hydrogen-Like Atoms 80
5–3 The Spectra of Alkali Metals 85
5–4 The Spectra of Alkaline Earths and Zn, Cd, and Hg 88
5–5 A More Physical Description of Atomic States 92
5–6 Summary 96
Problems 98

VI Atomic Excitation Probabilities 99

6–1 Lifetimes of Excited States 99
6–2 Kinetic Theory of Gases 107
6–3 Summary 111
Problems 113

VII Collisional Processes Involving Excited Atoms 115

7–1 Sensitized Fluorescence 117
7–2 Energy Resonance 122
7–3 Interconversions between Atomic Levels 126

7–4 The Association of Excited and Unexcited Atoms 128
7–5 Summary 131

VIII The Behavior of Atoms in Magnetic Fields 133

8–1 Relation between Electric Current and Magnetic Fields 133
8–2 The Zeeman Effect for Singlet States 134
8–3 Zeeman Splitting and the Gyromagnetic Ratio of Atoms 136
8–4 Experimental Confirmation of Space Quantization 139
8–5 Summary 142

IX Some of the Forces between Atoms: The Simplest Molecules 145

9–1 Van der Waals Interaction 145
9–2 Resonance Coupling 146
9–3 Vibrational States 149
9–4 Atoms in Molecules 154

Suggested Readings 155

Index 157

Units

Physical constants and communications between various units.

Avogadro number	$N = 6.025 \times 10^{23}$ molecules/mole
Electronic charge	$e = 4.802 \times 10^{-10}$ e.s.u.
Electronic mass	$m = 9.106 \times 10^{-28}$ g
Mass of proton	$m_p = 1.66 \times 10^{-24}$ g
Speed of light, in vacuo	$c = 2.998 \times 10^{10}$ cm/sec
Planck's constant	$h = 6.624 \times 10^{-27}$ erg-sec
Gas constant	$R = 1.987$ cal/deg/mole
Refractive index of air in sodium yellow light	$n = 1.000294$

Unit	*eV*	*cm*$^{-1}$	*erg/molecule*	*kcal/mole*
1 electron volt	1	8068.3	1.602×10^{-12}	23.063
1 cm^{-1}	1.239×10^{-4}	1	1.986×10^{-16}	2.858×10^{-3}
1 erg/molecule	6.242×10^{11}	5.036×10^{15}	1	1.440×10^{13}
1 kcal/mole	4.336×10^{-2}	3.50×10^{2}	6.946×10^{-14}	1

I

Atomic Spectra

LIGHT AND ITS INTERACTIONS with matter have probably provided the greatest single contribution to our present-day understanding of the detailed structure of atoms and molecules. Light has enabled us to see atomic phenomena. Our eyes detect only visible radiation, but scientific ingenuity has devised numerous artificial eyes, or detectors, that can see a vast range of the electromagnetic spectrum. The interaction of radiation with matter brings about changes in the radiation beam as well as in the material; normally the radiation loses energy while the material absorbs energy. Thus with the help of suitable detectors and instruments that can energy-analyze the radiation, experimental scientists have managed to explore the innermost depths of matter. Stimulated by the resulting experimental relationships, theoreticians have formulated physical laws and relationships that provide for a rational explanation of phenomena.

It is a sign of our times that an adequate theoretical equipment is not made available to a student as he acquires experimental insight. However, invaluable intuitive understanding of a so-called complex theory can be gleaned from a careful appraisal of the relationship between experiment and simple models arising from theory. All experimental scientists are thrilled by the discovery of beautiful phenomena, but the ultimate admiration of nature's works begins to emerge when some explanation is at hand.

To comprehend how atoms can unite to form molecules and how molecules can interact chemically, we must first understand the microscopic composition of atoms. The foundation of chemical knowledge is atomic composition. Each atom consists of a certain number of electrons, protons, and neutrons. From this basis and with the help of physical laws, we must derive a description of how atoms combine and influence one another. The development of a dynamic description of atomic structure requires a theory that can explain the detailed mechanics of the interplay of negative electrons with one another and with positively charged nuclei. In addition, the theory must provide a basis for the description of experimental facts.

Much of the early understanding of electrons in atoms came from experimental studies of **atomic spectroscopy.** Spectroscopy[1] deals with the measurement of certain effects resulting from the interaction of various kinds of energy with matter. Atomic spectroscopy usually means *the study of interactions between atoms and electromagnetic radiation.* We shall examine many of these measurements, but first we must see how the experiments are performed and the manner in which the experimental results are conveniently expressed.

1-1 ELEMENTARY PRINCIPLES

At the beginning of certain chapters there will appear a section such as this, containing some fundamental background material that is necessary for an understanding of what follows in the chapter. This introductory material is more fully discussed in the larger elementary texts listed at the end of the book.

Elementary Particles

The electron is a negatively charged particle of small mass ($m = 9.1 \times 10^{-28}$ g) compared with the mass of the positively charged nucleus (mass of proton $\approx$ mass of neutron $= 1.67 \times 10^{-24}$ g). The atom is composed of a nucleus and electrons. The

[1] From the Latin *spectrum*, image, and the Greek *skopein*, to view.

average space occupied by electrons is very much greater than the nuclear volume; in fact, the size of the atom may usually be taken as the effective size of the electron distribution.

Electromagnetic Radiation

Electromagnetic radiation is so called because its propagation past a point causes both electric and magnetic disturbances at the point. We need describe only one of these disturbances. Choosing the magnetic disturbance at the point, we find that the magnetic field strength builds up in time, reaches a maximum, then decays through zero, decreases further, producing a magnetic field opposite to the previous one (as when the north and south poles of a magnet are interchanged), reaches a maximum in this direction, and then increases to zero and starts the cycle once again.

We can represent this travelling disturbance by means of wave diagrams, as in Fig. 1–1. The disturbing wave is propagating along

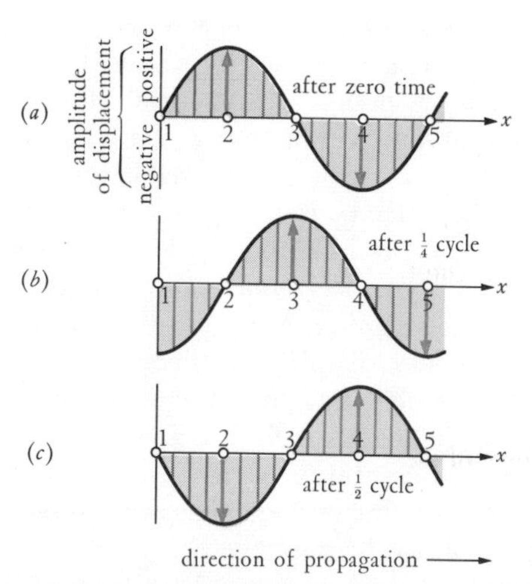

Figure 1–1 Representation of a transverse disturbance by a wave frozen at three instants in time *t*. (*a*) $t = 0$, (*b*) $t = \frac{1}{4}$ cycle, (*c*) $t = \frac{1}{2}$ cycle. The wave is propagating along the *x* direction.

the x direction, but the disturbance acts at right angles to the direction of propagation (hence the term **transverse wave**), say along the z axis. The series of points 0, 1, 2, 3, . . . , etc., are distributed along the direction of propagation. Imagine the wave frozen in the position of the curve in Fig. 1–1*a*. After zero time ($t = 0$) point 1 experiences no field, point 2 a maximum positive field, point 3 no field, point 4 a maximum negative field, and so on. After one-quarter of the above cycle, the situation has changed, and the curve in Fig. 1–1*b* represents the frozen wave. Now points 2 and 4 experience no field, and 1 and 5 have a maximum negative disturbance. After one-half cycle, points 1 and 3 are again at zero field, and points 2 and 4 experience fields of the same magnitude but of different sign from those at $t = 0$.

The time for one cycle is known as the **period** of the oscillating disturbance. The number of cycles that occur in every second is known as the **frequency** of the oscillation. The distance that the wave is propagated during one cycle is known as the **wavelength** of the wave. The **wave amplitude** at a point along the horizontal axis is the magnitude of the disturbance at that point. Clearly, if the wave propagates a distance of one wavelength during one cycle, the velocity of the wave along the x direction of propagation must be one wavelength per period. Symbolically the velocity v is expressed as $v = \lambda\nu$, where λ (lambda) is the wavelength in length units and ν (nu) is the frequency measured in number of cycles per second (cps). The velocity is then given in length per second, whatever length units are used to describe the wavelength.

As indicated above, electromagnetic radiation is more complicated than our description of a magnetic disturbance; besides the transverse magnetic disturbance there is an analogous transverse electric disturbance that provides a fluctuating electric field at right angles to the magnetic field at a point in the path of the wave. The wave representation of electromagnetic radiation at an instant in time is shown in Fig. 1–2. The electric and magnetic disturbances are **in phase** because the point experiences maximum or minimum or zero disturbance from both fields at the same time (i.e., the disturbances arrive at the same time).

The velocity of electromagnetic waves is a constant in a given

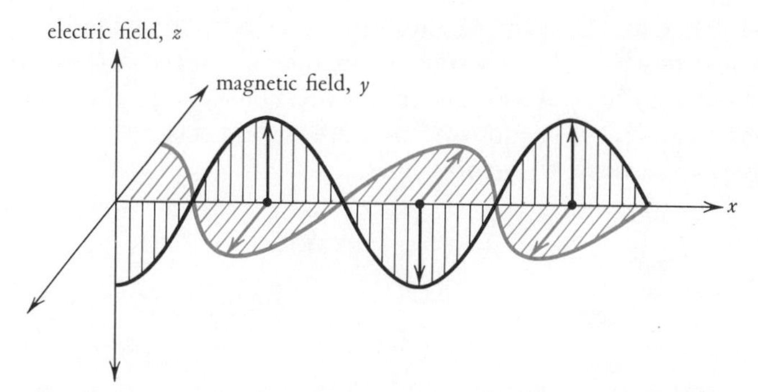

Figure 1–2 Transverse electromagnetic waves. (*a*) The electric disturbance is in the plane *xz*, the magnetic disturbance in the plane *xy*. The direction of propagation is *x*.

medium; the frequency of the disturbance is in inverse proportionality to the wavelength:

$$\nu = \frac{c}{\lambda} \tag{1-1}$$

where c is the velocity of light in vacuo (3×10^{10} cm/sec). Since electromagnetic waves do not travel with the same velocity in all media, the above equation is strictly true only in a vacuum, as noted. The ratio of the velocity of electromagnetic waves in vacuo to their velocity in a given medium is a constant known as the **refractive index** of the medium. Substituting nv for c in Eq. (1–1), where n is the refractive index and v is the velocity of waves in the medium, we reach the equation

$$\lambda\nu = nv = c \tag{1-2}$$

It is not immediately clear from Eq. (1–2) whether λ or ν or both λ and ν are dependent on the refractive index. It turns out that the frequency of the wave motion is independent of the medium but the wavelength changes with refractive index n. Frequency is therefore the invariant property of electromagnetic radiation. Since spectroscopic measurements are usually made by measuring wavelengths of radiation, the refractive index of the medium in which the experiments are conducted (usually air) must be known in order to obtain frequency values from the measurements. So-called vacuum wavelengths λ_0 are related to measured values λ_n through the expressions

$$\lambda_0 = \frac{c}{\nu} = \frac{nv}{\nu} = n\lambda_n$$

or

$$\left(\frac{\lambda_0}{\lambda_n}\right) = n \qquad \textbf{(1–3)}$$

which indicates that if $n > 1$, $\lambda_0 > \lambda_n$: the wavelengths measured are less than the vacuum wavelengths.

The wavelength of green light is about 5×10^{-5} cm. Since numbers of this magnitude are unwieldy for everyday use, light wavelengths are usually measured in Angstrom units (A) where

$$1 \text{ A} = 10^{-8} \text{ cm}$$

Thus green light has a wavelength of about 5000 A. Angstrom units are convenient for distances at the atomic level, since atomic diameters and chemical bonds are always just a few Angstroms in length.

Energy Relationships

Electromagnetic radiation can also be regarded as corpuscular. Instead of the travelling disturbance described above, the radiation can be considered a stream of energy packets or particles travelling with the velocity of light. These energy packets are called **photons.** The frequency of wave motion ν is related to the energy of the photons E through Planck's equation

$$E = h\nu \qquad \textbf{(1–4)}$$

where h is **Planck's constant.** Utilizing Eqs. (1–3) and (1–4), the energy can be written

$$E = hc/\lambda_0 \qquad \textbf{(1–5)}$$

λ_0 is given in centimeters, c in centimeters per second. The energy in the cgs (centimeter-gram-second) system of units is expressed as ergs per molecule. Planck's constant is therefore in units of erg-seconds, written as erg-sec. It has the value 6.624×10^{-27} erg-sec. E is the energy of one quantum of radiation of frequency ν.

Later it will be seen that the *energy of a state* and not the *frequency of electronic oscillations* is the important quantity that spectroscopists measure. Thus it is convenient to plan to discuss spectra in terms of a wave characteristic that is proportional to energy—notably, the number of waves per centimeter, otherwise known as the **wavenumber** $\bar{\nu}$. Thus

$$\bar{\nu} = \frac{1}{\lambda_0}$$

and the energy is related to $\bar{\nu}$ as follows:

$$E = (hc)\bar{\nu} \tag{1-6}$$

where (hc) is a universal constant. The units of $\bar{\nu}$ are reciprocal centimeters, written as cm^{-1}. Another reason why wavenumbers have been used as an energy unit—rather than ergs, for example—is that $\bar{\nu}$ can be obtained independently of the velocity of light in vacuo. Since the refractive index at any wavelength can be measured independently to almost any degree of accuracy, we have $\bar{\nu} = 1/n\lambda_n$; thus $\bar{\nu}$ is given in terms of λ_n, which could be obtained to a higher degree of accuracy than c.

1–2 EXPERIMENTAL SPECTROSCOPY

Spectral Analysis and Absorption Spectroscopy

When light that is spectrally continuous (for example, light from a hot filament lamp) is passed through an atomic vapor, it is found that the emergent light is no longer continuous. It is therefore certain that the incident electromagnetic radiation interacts with the atoms in the chamber. Certain details of this interaction can be obtained by spectrally analyzing the emergent light and comparing the resultant spectrum with that of the incident light source.

A spectral analysis involves the dispersion of the light by

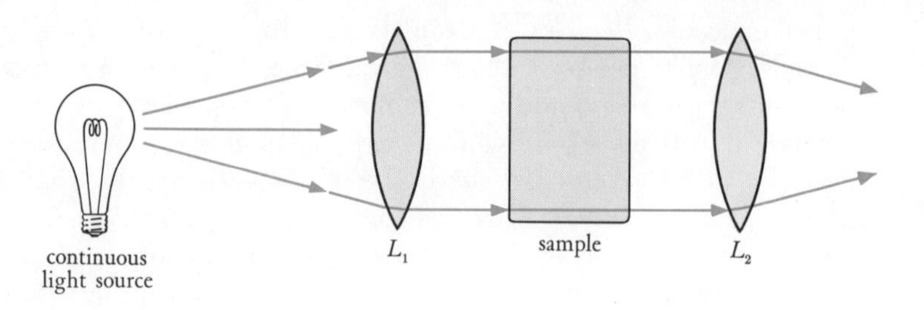

Figure 1–3 Standard experimental arrangement for obtaining an absorption spectrum. Lens L_1 collects the divergent light and produces a parallel beam; L_2 focuses the parallel light onto the slit. From slit to photographic

prisms or its diffraction by diffraction gratings. A prism P, such as the one shown in Fig. 1–3, will disperse an incident beam into its component colors (wavelengths). The missing wavelengths, removed from the continuum by the atomic sample, can be measured by moving a light-sensitive detector across the dispersed beam or by permitting the dispersed beam to fall on a photographic plate Ph.

In the latter case the developed plate will have dark and light regions corresponding to spectral regions with high and low intensity, respectively, in the incident beam. Light that falls on one part of the plate will differ in energy from light that falls on another. Thus by placing an appropriate scale along the exposed plate, the relative energies of the different spectral regions may be obtained. As we have seen, the energy of electromagnetic radiation is related to the frequency and to the wavelength of the radiation. Normally spectra are reproduced in the form of graphs of intensity, or extent of plate blackening, vs. wavelength or wavenumber.

Plate I shows the results of some typical absorption experiments. The absorption spectrum of the atomic vapor is ob-

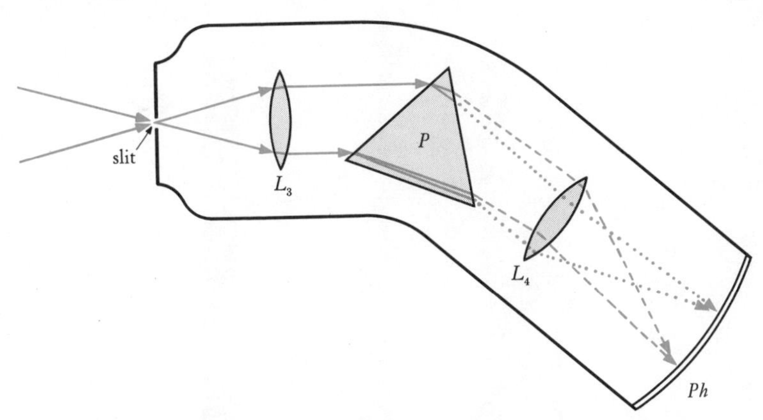

plate encompasses the components of a prism spectrograph, viz., lenses L_3 and L_4 in conjunction with the prism P. The lenses and prism must be made of material that does not absorb light in the spectral region of interest.

tained by interposing the vapor between the source and the entrance to the spectrograph. Notice that a series of **characteristic absorption lines** is obtained. The energies and sequence of the lines from one type of atom are typical of that atom and differ from the spectrum of any other atom. Hence we already have a way to distinguish one atom from another. Experimental atomic absorption spectroscopy leads to the following conclusions:

1. Each atom interacts with electromagnetic radiation in a unique manner.

2. The atom is influenced by electromagnetic radiation of *certain definite energies*; hence the appearance of *line spectra* superimposed on the otherwise unaffected background that is due to the continuous light source.

3. The energies of the absorption lines must relate to some invariant physical property of the individual atoms.

Emission Spectroscopy

It has been known for many years that a characteristic glow, or emission, is obtained from atomic gases that are subjected to

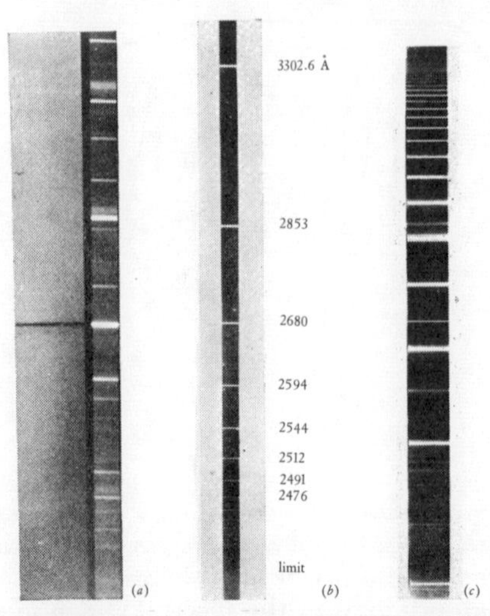

Plate I (*a*) Absorption by mercury vapor at 2537 A. The 2537-A line is shown as a light line on a darker background as it would be on the photographic plate. The upper-line spectrum is a portion of the emission spectrum of mercury illustrating the coincidence of absorption and emission lines at 2537 A. [From P. D. Foote and F. L. Mohler, *The Origin of Spectra,* Chemical Catalog, New York, 1922, Fig. 14A.] (*b*) Absorption spectrum of sodium vapor. [From H. G. Kuhn, *Atomic Spectra,* Academic, New York, 1962, plate 4.] (*c*) Spectrum of Zeta Tauri from H_γ to Balmer series limit, made with 37.5-inch reflector. These are all absorption lines reversed against the continuous background of the stellar emission spectrum. This series can appear in absorption because the first excited state of H is appreciably populated at the temperature of this star. [From Foote and Mohler, *op. cit.*, Fig. 17.]

strong electrical potentials. Such systems are called **discharge sources** and have commercial use in, for example, the sodium street lamp and the neon discharge tube. A spectral analysis of the emission from a discharge source can be performed by replacing the light source of the spectrograph arrangement in Fig. 1–3 by a discharge lamp. Once again a series of lines is produced on the

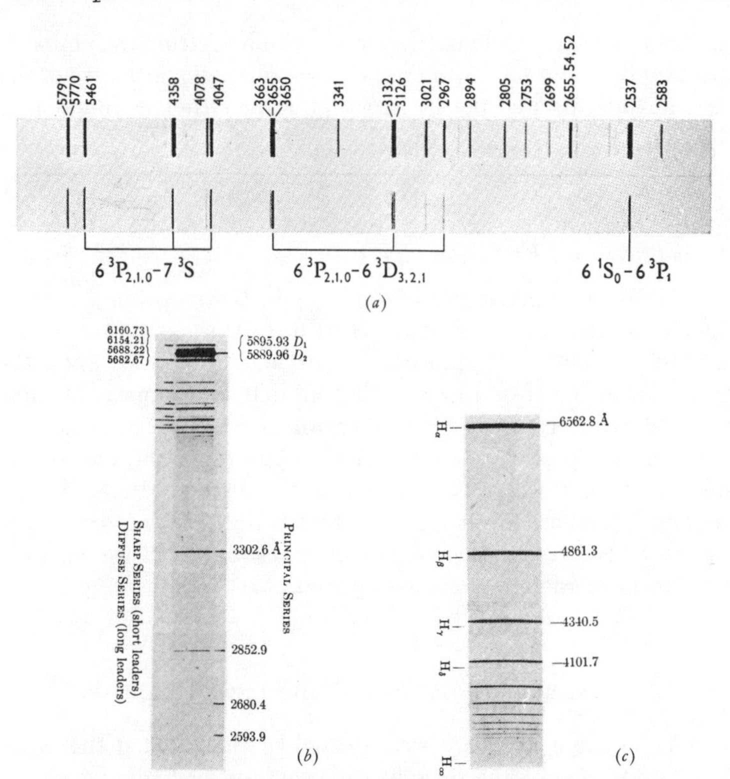

Plate II (*a*) Emission spectrum of mercury; upper, long exposure; lower, short exposure. [From H. G. Kuhn, *Atomic Spectra,* Academic, New York, 1962, plate 7.] (*b*) Emission spectrum of sodium. Three series can be recognized and one of them (principal series) corresponds to the absorption series of Plate I*b*. [From G. Herzberg, *Atomic Spectra and Atomic Structure,* Dover, New York, 1944, Fig. 3.] (*c*) Balmer emission series of hydrogen atoms. [From Herzberg, *op. cit.,* Fig. 1.]

photographic plate. In this experiment, of course, the lines are the blackened regions of the plate.

Plate II shows some examples of line emission spectra. Discharge spectra usually exhibit many more lines than the absorption spectra of the same atoms. In addition to line structure, emission spectra often contain continuous regions where the intensity of the light passing through the spectrograph is a continuous function of the energy.

Relationship between Absorption and Emission Spectra

Although many more lines appear in the emission spectrum than in the absorption spectrum, there are certain lines that appear in both. As before, the lines are identifiable because we know the energy at which they appear. Certain lines that appear in emission and in absorption are named **resonance lines.** For example, the mercury line at 2537 A, which appears in the absorption spectrum of Plate I*a* and in the emission spectrum of Plate II*a*, is a mercury resonance line. The light that is emitted by atoms at the energy of the resonance line is called **resonance fluorescence,** resonance emission, or resonance radiation.

1–3 SERIES RELATIONS FOR SPECTRAL LINES

As long ago as 1885 it was realized by Balmer that the wavelengths of some of the lines in the spectrum of hydrogen atoms could be fitted to a mathematical series. The lines extend from the red (15,000 cm^{-1}) to the ultraviolet region (28,000 cm^{-1}) of the spectrum, and about 35 of them have since been observed and fitted to Rydberg's (1890) modification of Balmer's formula, which gives the wavenumber $\bar{\nu}_2$ of the line:

$$\bar{\nu}_2 = R\left(\frac{1}{4} - \frac{1}{m^2}\right) \tag{1–7}$$

where R, known now as the **Rydberg constant,** has the value of 109,737.31 cm^{-1} and m takes only integral values greater than 2 (i.e., $m = 3, 4, 5, \ldots, 35$). Figure 1–4 is a schematic diagram of this hydrogen-atom emission spectrum. The lines become closer together as the energy increases; according to the formula of Eq. (1–7), if we put m equal to infinity ($1/m^2 = 0$), we should find the

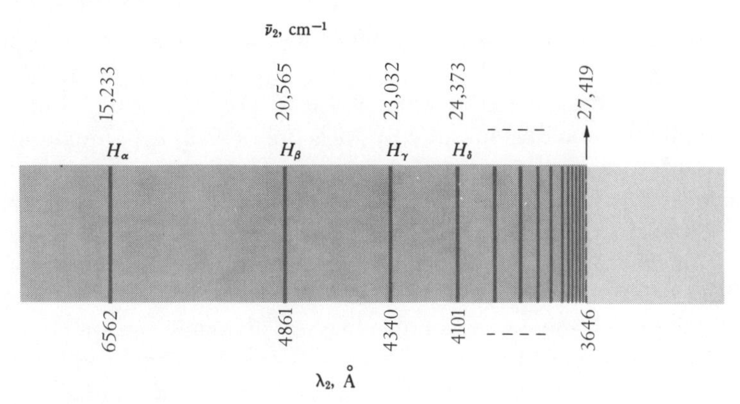

Figure 1–4 Schematic diagram of the Balmer series of hydrogen.

position of the limit of this series of lines. This is represented in the diagram as a dashed line at $R/4 = 27{,}419$ cm^{-1}. In the region of this limit the successive lines become so close together that the spectrum appears to be continuous.

Later, Paschen (1909) photographed another series of lines from hydrogen, which appeared in the infrared region and whose wavenumbers are obtained from the formula

$$\bar{\nu}_3 = R\left(\frac{1}{9} - \frac{1}{m^2}\right) \qquad \text{where } m = 4, 5, 6, \text{etc.} \qquad (1\text{–}8)$$

This time the series limit is at $R/9$ cm^{-1}. Another series was uncovered by Lyman (1906), in the ultraviolet:

$$\bar{\nu}_1 = R\left(1 - \frac{1}{m^2}\right) \qquad \text{where } m = 2, 3, 4, \text{etc.} \qquad (1\text{–}9)$$

Obviously each series fits one formula, which has been anticipated by our use of the subscripts on $\bar{\nu}$. Generally, the wavenumber of any known line in the normal spectrum of atomic hydrogen is given by

$$\bar{\nu}_n = R\left(\frac{1}{n^2} - \frac{1}{m^2}\right) \qquad (1\text{–}10)$$

where m is any integer that is greater than n. The limit of the nth series lies at R/n^2 cm^{-1}.

The empirical relationship of Eq. (1–10) was given fundamental theoretical significance by Niels Bohr (1913) in his quantum theory of the line spectra of hydrogen. Bohr deduced the expression by introducing certain postulates that will be discussed later. Suffice it to say at this point that the experimental value of R was within one part in one hundred thousand of a value calculated from known physical constants.

Although there was no unified theory of atomic spectra before 1913 and the Bohr theory, the discovery of special series to which most spectral lines could be assigned represented considerable progress in understanding. Certain considerations based on Planck's theory led to the conclusion that, during the process of absorption and emission, the atoms were undergoing *quantum transitions between states of different energy.* This conclusion becomes more apparent if Eq. (1–10) is multiplied on both sides by Planck's constant h, remembering that the energy ΔE_n of the quantum of wavenumber $\bar{\nu}_n$ is $h\bar{\nu}_n c$. Thus

$$\Delta E_n = h\bar{\nu}_n c = hRc\left(\frac{1}{n^2} - \frac{1}{m^2}\right) \qquad \textit{(1–11)}$$

The right-hand side of Eq. (1–11) is the difference between the two terms hRc/n^2 and hRc/m^2, each of which is an energy.

The integers n and m refer to the lower and upper (higher) energy states, respectively. A Rydberg emission series refers to *transitions from a manifold of upper states to one given lower state* characterized by n. The two energy terms n and m are not on a proper energy scale, since $1/n^2$ is always greater than $1/m^2$ for a given series. This ambiguity arises because we are now considering energies rather than energy differences.

A convenient energy scale is obtained by placing the energy of these states at *minus* the expressions given above; i.e.,

$$\epsilon_n = -hcR/n^2$$
$$\epsilon_m = -hcR/m^2$$

where n and m have the same meaning as before. This is equivalent to having the zero of energy refer to the state for which $m = \infty$. All the lower-lying states have negative energies in relation to this zero. Thus in the Lyman series of lines the final state for all transitions is located at $\epsilon(n = 1) = -hcR$; in the Balmer series the final state is located at $\epsilon(n = 2) = -hcR/4$. Notice that $\epsilon(n = 2)$ is at higher energy than $\epsilon(n = 1)$ by the amount $\frac{3}{4}hcR$.

The introduction of this energy scale involves some interpretation of the atomic processes described. The assignment of the terms characterized by n and m to different states of the atom anticipates the results of Bohr's theory of 1913, which in fact did not appear until 23 years after the Rydberg formula and seven years after the discovery of the Lyman series.

These ideas account for the difference in the complexity of absorption and emission spectra as reflected in the number of observed lines. Atoms that are in their lowest possible energy states can only absorb radiation corresponding to the differences in energy between the *one lowest state* and the various upper states. These transitions give rise to a number of absorption lines (*one series*). Atoms that are induced to absorb energy by means of, say, an electrical discharge can arrive in a variety of upper states. The resulting emission from an atomic gas consists of lines corresponding to the energy gaps between these upper states and the *many lower states* (*many series*). The fact that there are many lines in the series is due to the fact that there are many atoms, each with many states. This is illustrated in Fig. 1–5.

This concept also explains the small number of coincidences between the emission and the absorption spectrum. Absorption lines correspond to *lowest*-state to upper-state transitions; thus coincidence between absorption and emission lines occurs only when the final state of the emission process is the lowest state of the atom.

The lowest or most stable state, and the upper states are conventionally called the **ground state** and the **excited states**, respectively. Each atomic system has only one ground state but has many excited states.

1–4 SUMMARY

In ending this chapter, it is appropriate to anticipate certain conclusions from later material. The Bohr theory for hydrogen

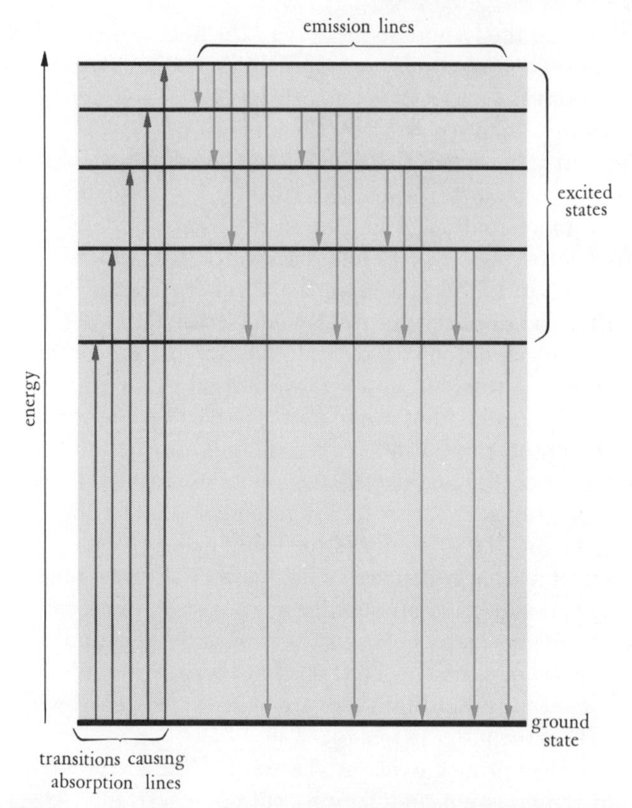

Figure 1-5 The relative complexity of absorption and emission spectra. For each absorption line there is a group of emission lines. One member of each group is coincident with an absorption line.

and the later wave mechanical theory for other atoms including hydrogen (1926) utilize the Planck energy-frequency relationship $E = h\nu$. However, the concept of quantum jumps, or transitions, as visualized by pre-Bohr physicists was in fact erroneous, inasmuch as the emphasis was on the *frequency* of electronic rotations. Planck regarded the energy E as relating to an electron oscillating at a definite frequency and held that only certain frequencies are permitted to occur in accordance with this relationship. The important view that came with Bohr is that only certain *energy states* of the electrons are permitted, which implies that atomic spectral data can tell us little in regard to the frequencies of oscillatory motion of electrons in atoms.

PROBLEMS

1. Calculate the wavenumbers (cm^{-1}) for the following wavelengths and indicate to which spectral region these waves belong, i.e., x-ray, ultraviolet, visible, infrared, microwave, or radiowave.

(*a*) 5000 A (*d*) 3 cm
(*b*) 2000 A (*e*) 1000 m
(*c*) 100,000 A (*f*) 1 A

2. Calculate the number of atoms in 1 cc of a gas that is at a pressure of 10^{-5} atm at 25°C. (R = 0.082 liter-atm/g-atom-deg; $N = 6.02 \times 10^{23}$)

3. What is the wavelength of electromagnetic radiation having the energy of 1 Rydberg?

4. Calculate the energy difference of the series limits for $\bar{\nu}_3$ and $\bar{\nu}_4$. What does this difference represent?

5. Calculate the Rydberg constant from the Balmer series data of Fig. 1–4.

6. What is the percentage error in wavenumber values obtained by neglecting to correct for the fact that measurements are made in air in the region of

(*a*) λ_n = 5000 A
(*b*) λ_n = 100,000 A
(*c*) λ_n = 500 A

(refractive index of air = 1.00029)

II

The Interactions between Atoms and Electrons

IN THE PREVIOUS CHAPTER the interaction between atomic systems and electromagnetic radiation was discussed. We discovered that experiments in optical spectroscopy did not permit a specification of the frequencies of electronic motion in the classical sense. The postulate (Bohr) that atoms have *a set of electronic states* and that quantum transitions can occur between these states was anticipated. Atomic systems can interact with other forms of energy.

2–1 ELECTRONS AND ELECTRON ENERGIES

It is possible to produce a beam of electron particles with a continuous range of energies analogous to electromagnetic waves, or a beam of photons. To do this, a filament is heated electrically by a battery, and a positively charged plate is placed close to the filament. Electrons on the surface of the filament metal will be attracted to the positive plate if the filament is sufficiently hot for some of the electrons to overcome the energy binding them to the

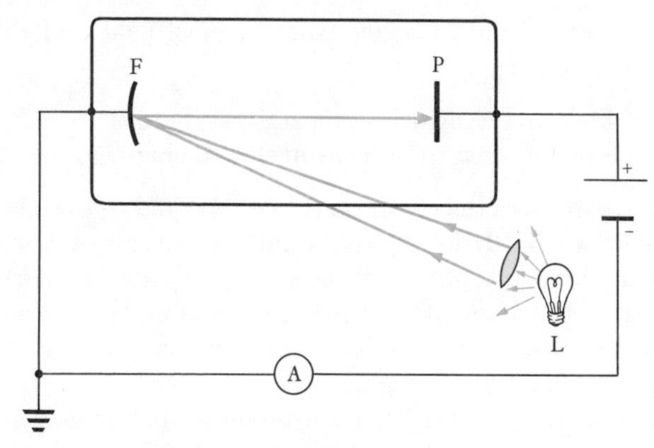

Figure 2–1 Schematic diagram of simple tube and circuit to demonstrate photoelectron ejection.

surface of the filament metal. In this manner electrons may be caused to flow through the evacuated space between the plate and the filament.

The relationship between photon energies and electron energies is clearer if it is realized that photons may actually cause the ejection of electrons from a metallic surface. Consider the apparatus of Fig. 2–1. The filament F and plate P have an electrical-potential difference between them produced by the battery. The plate is electrically positive with respect to the filament. In this experiment, however, no electrons will pass across the evacuated space between the filament and the plate because the filament is not heated. Light, a photon beam, is directed at the filament. If electrons pass across the gap, they will be detected by the electric current that will flow in the external circuit; hence the presence of an electric-current-measuring device A in the circuit. As the incident photon energy ($E = h\nu$) is gradually increased, a point will be reached when current just begins to flow. If the light is switched off, then the current will stop. This current is called a **photocurrent** and must arise because of the ejection of electrons from the metal by the impact of photons. The law of conservation of energy requires that following equality must hold near the surface of the filament:

(energy of liberated electron) = (energy of photon)
− (energy required to liberate an electron having zero energy)

The last term in the equation is exactly equal to the energy of the **photothreshold;** i.e., it is the photon energy that will *just* produce a photocurrent. This is a property of the particular metal used in the filament, and the amount of energy is known as the **work function.** The work functions of many materials lie in the energy range of visible light.

It can also be shown that each photon in the beam (each quantum of electromagnetic radiation) *is capable of producing just one electron.* This lends physical meaning to the corpuscular nature of electromagnetic radiation. The dual nature of light and the above photoelectric effects were conjectured by Einstein (1905).

We must now answer the question of the nature of the energy contained by the electron. We know that the electron is negatively charged and has a definite mass; what occurs when it acquires energy? A macroscopic body, such as a tennis ball, acquires the most energy of motion when it is struck with the greatest force. The type of energy that obtains because of motion is known as **kinetic energy.** Explicitly, the kinetic energy (K.E.) of a particle of mass m is given by

$$\text{K.E.} = \tfrac{1}{2}\, mv^2 \qquad (2\text{–}1)$$

where v is the velocity of the particle. Interpreting the previous discussion in these terms, we conclude that high-energy photons produce high-velocity photoejected electrons. It is clear from this that as an electron accelerates through space from the filament to the positive plate its velocity, and hence its energy, is increasing throughout its journey. Consequently the electrons do not arrive at the plate with the same energy they had at the surface of the filament metal. This process represents the transformation of *electric potential energy*, contained by electrons at the filament, into *electron kinetic energy*. Electric potential is normally measured in volts, and if the potential due to the battery in Fig. 2–1 is V volts, the electron acquires precisely V electron volts of energy during its journey from filament to plate. We must have some method of translating electron volts (eV) into our spectroscopic units of energy, i.e., cm^{-1}. In fact, as we shall later prove,

$$1 \text{ eV} = 8067 \text{ cm}^{-1} \tag{2-2}$$

We may use either of these energy units to describe atomic processes.

Collisions

We shall define two types of collision:

1. **Elastic collision,** where the colliding particles have the same total kinetic energy before and after collision, i.e., where kinetic energy is conserved. Ordinary macroscopic collisions between billiard balls are examples of elastic collisions.
2. **Inelastic collision,** where the total energy is conserved but some kinetic energy is converted into potential energy, or internal energy of one of the particles.

The inelastic collision of an electron with an atom can result in the electronic excitation of the atom. The energy-balance equation for this process would be

$$\begin{aligned}&(\text{K.E. of electron}) + (\text{K.E. of ground-state atom})\\&= (\text{K.E. of excited atom}) + (\text{energy of electronic excitation})\\&+ (\text{K.E. of electron after collision})\end{aligned} \tag{2-3}$$

Because the atom is so much heavier than the electron, we may assume that the velocity, and hence the kinetic energy, of the atom is not affected by the collision with the electron. Hence the energy-balance equation may be written

$$\begin{aligned}&(\text{K.E. of electron}) = (\text{excitation energy of atom})\\&+ (\text{K.E. of electron after collision})\end{aligned} \tag{2-4}$$

Ionization Potentials

The energy required to completely remove an electron from an atom is the **ionization potential,** often referred to as the ionization energy. The energy supply for ionization of an atom can be derived from photons, energetic electrons, or any other adequate source. Because the ionization potential measures the energy required to remove an electron, it automatically refers to the energy liberated when an electron is incorporated into an ion. Thus it refers to the binding energy of that electron in the atom. Direct measurements of ionization potentials are often obtained from electron-impact experiments, and it has become customary to use the electron volt as a unit for these energies. Ionizations caused by photon-atom interactions are called **photoionizations.**

2–2 THE BOHR ATOM

Although ultimately superseded by a more precise mechanics (the quantum mechanics, 1926), the **Bohr theory** bridged an enormous gap in the early twentieth-century understanding of atoms. Prior to this, the Planck theory accounted for the existence of radiation from atoms in the sense that it predicted that charged particles oscillating at a particular frequency ν would radiate photons of energy $h\nu$.

But the existence of discrete line spectra could not be rationalized on the basis of classical mechanics. To account for atomic spectral lines, Bohr rejected the idea that electrons in atoms behave like continuous oscillators and proposed instead that the atom can exist only in definite *discrete stationary states* with energies E_0, E_1, E_2, . . . , etc. The energies of spectral lines are those for which $h\nu$ has precisely the value that can raise the atom from one stationary state to another.

For completeness we shall state the three postulates proposed by Bohr in 1913.

1. *The electrons move in circular orbits around the central atomic nucleus.*

2. *Only certain discrete orbits are permitted*, and *the electrons radiate no energy when they are in these orbits.* These concepts are contrary to the classical theory of charged particles. According to the older theory an electron moving in an orbit would radiate, thus losing energy and continuously changing its orbit.

3. *A quantum of radiation is emitted or absorbed when an electron jumps from one discrete orbit to another.*

Bohr later developed the **correspondence principle.** This principle provides for continuity between the new mechanics for atomic systems and the older classical mechanics. Basically, it states that as the dimensions of the atomic systems increase, or as the radii of the proposed electron orbits increase, the new mechanics must yield to classical mechanics. This implies that, in this limit, quantized states will go over into continuous states.

There are three important experimental verifications of these ideas. The first two (below) are optical, and the third (Sec. 2–3) is an independent direct confirmation of Bohr's postulate on the existence of discrete energy levels in the atom.

The Combination Principle

Within the framework of Bohr's theory, atoms can be excited into higher electronic stationary states $E_1, E_2, \ldots$, etc. from the ground state E_0. After excitation to any state the atoms will spontaneously emit radiation.

Suppose the initial excited state is that with energy E_3 (see Fig. 2–2). The excitation from E_0 to E_3 is represented by a vertical dashed arrow from the horizontal line at energy E_0 to the horizontal line at energy E_3. Some atoms will emit light corresponding to the transition from the state with energy E_3 to that with energy E_0. We call this the $3 \rightarrow 0$ transition. The transitions $3 \rightarrow 1$ and $3 \rightarrow 2$ are also possible. After the transition $3 \rightarrow 2$ the same atom may emit again during a $2 \rightarrow 1$ or $2 \rightarrow 0$ transition. Thus a large number of emission lines should be observed. However, it must be possible to choose a certain series of lines such that the sum of their energies is exactly equal to the energy of the highest energy line. This simply means the combined energy of the processes $3 \rightarrow 2 \rightarrow 1 \rightarrow 0$ must equal the energy of $3 \rightarrow 0$. Indeed it is possible to find such series of lines in atomic emission spectra, and this was done by Ritz (1905) for many spectra before the theoretical implications were realized. Thus the **Ritz combination principle** is a direct confirmation of the Bohr theory of stationary states in atoms.

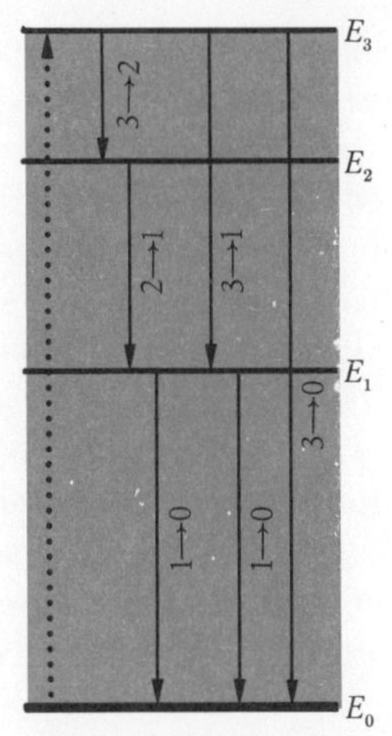

Figure 2–2 A set of energy levels. Each horizontal line is *a representation* of a Bohr stationary state energy. In reality this is a one-dimensional graph with energy plotted on a vertical scale.

Discrete and Continuous Atomic Spectra

Each stationary state of the atom in the Bohr theory corresponds to a particular fixed orbit for the electron moving about the nucleus. When moving in this orbit, the electron does not radiate; it only does so when its stationary state is changed. The interpretation of the terms in Eq. (1–10) leads to the conclusion that in a particular series of lines, e.g., the Balmer series, the spacing between the lines will quadratically decrease as the energy of the line increases, finally reaching a series limit. It is found that the absorption spectra of atoms form similar series with quadratic spacings and series limits, but at energies beyond the series limit, i.e., the limit of the line spectrum, the atom still absorbs light. The absorption spectrum beyond the series limit is *continuous*. Plate I shows the absorption spectra of certain atoms, and one can clearly see series of lines that tend toward a limit. As we shall see later, absorption of energies corresponding to the continuum gives rise to *ionization* of the atom. Consequently that region of the spectrum is known as the **ionization continuum.**

The physical interpretation of the two terms in the series formula is that the fixed one (with n) indicates the type of orbit (e.g., its energy and size) in which the electron finally resides. The second, variable term (with m) indicates the nature of the orbit from which the electron is transferred during the transition. So m gauges the physical extent of the orbit of the excited electron. As m becomes larger, successive lines become closer and the electron orbit increases in size. Toward the series limit there are a very large number of lines within a small energy region; thus we have a quasi-continuum. In other words, as the effective size of the system increases by excitation of the electron further and further from the nucleus, the quantum condition for the existence of discrete energy states becomes less and less clear. Near the series limit the energy states are nearly continuous, corresponding to the classical description of an accelerating electron as a continuous emitter. Thus the spectra confirm the Bohr correspondence principle discussed earlier.

2–3 ELECTRON-ATOM-COLLISION EXPERIMENTS

Franck and Hertz (1914) obtained conclusive proof of the existence of discrete electronic excited states of atoms. Their method involved the use of controlled collisions of electrons with mercury atoms. The apparatus is shown schematically in Fig. 2–3.

As the electrical potential V_p between the filament F and the anode electron collector P is increased, more electrons arrive at the anode during a given interval, and the electric current I_p, measured by a galvanometer, increases. If a small pressure of mercury vapor (or another atomic gas) is maintained between the electrodes, the electrons traversing the space between filament and anode will undergo collisions with the vapor atoms. Atomic sizes are large enough for electron-atom collisions to be probable at pressures of gas well below 1 atm. The two important parameters in these experiments are the anode current I_p, which measures the number of electrons arriving at the anode per unit of time, and the electrical potential between anode and filament, which determines the energy spectrum of the electrons that arrive at the anode.

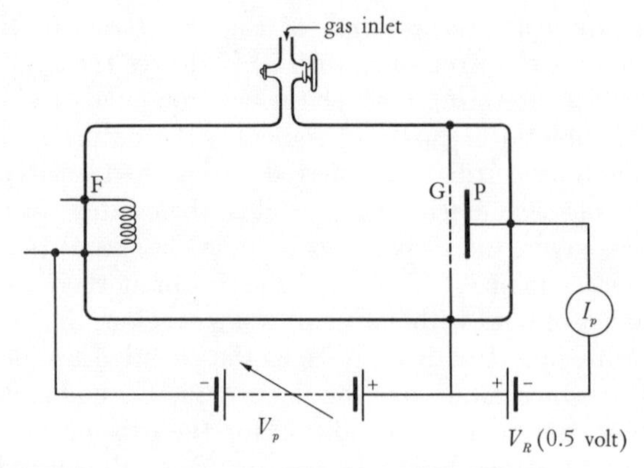

Figure 2–3 A schematic diagram of the apparatus for the Franck-Hertz experiment.

A grid G is placed close to the anode in the actual experiment. This is constructed from an open wire mesh that does not interfere with the passage of electrons. The grid is kept at a slight positive electrical potential with respect to the anode such that electrons reaching the anode must have arrived at the grid with sufficient kinetic energy to overcome the potential difference between the grid and the anode. This potential is usually about 0.5 volt and is called a **retarding potential** V_R.

The results of such an experiment are best discussed with reference to a graph of anode current vs. electron energy. Figure 2–4*a* shows schematically such a plot for the Franck-Hertz experiment with mercury atoms. As the electrical potential is increased, the the current increases in region A of the curve. At B, the current starts to decrease with increasing electron energy. Here, many electrons must have lost their kinetic energy through inelastic collisions with mercury atoms. As the electron energy is increased still further, the current increases again, in region C; at D, another drop in current is observed.

The energy at which the current drops off at D is just twice the energy at which the initial decrease at B occurred. For mercury atoms these energies are 4.85 and 9.8 eV. The experiment shows

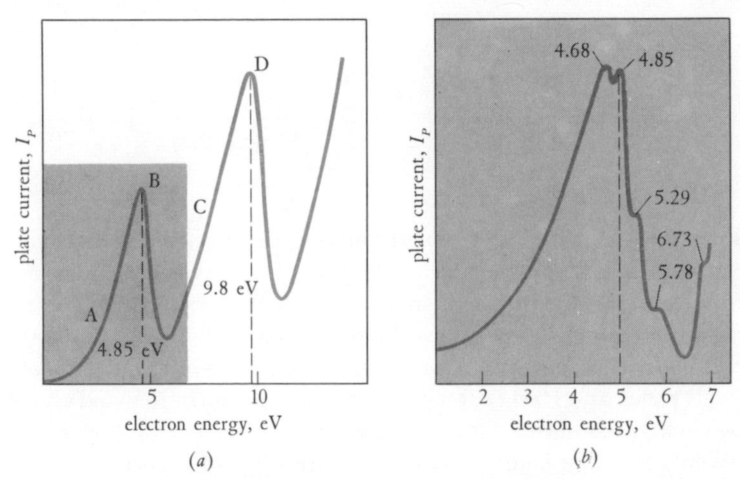

Figure 2–4 Representation of results from the Franck-Hertz experiment on mercury vapor.

that electrons can undergo inelastic collisions with mercury atoms only when they have at least 4.85 eV of kinetic energy. At energies less than 4.85 eV, the collisions are elastic, and because of the small mass of the electrons, very little kinetic energy is lost during collisions. Consequently the current rises with increasing electron energy. At 4.85 eV the electrons begin to undergo inelastic collisions; therefore mercury atoms must have a *stationary electronic excited state* at 4.85 eV above the ground state. Thus mercury atoms can absorb excitation energy in units, or quanta, of 4.85 eV. This is why the current rises again as the electrons gain energy in excess of the critical amount. When the electron energy just reaches 9.8 eV, an electron can undergo successive inelastic collisions with two mercury atoms, giving 4.85 eV to each; therefore the current decreases in this region.

In the absorption spectrum of mercury vapor there is a strong line at 2537 A (see Plate I). This line is also observed in the emission spectrum (see Plate II). The change in energy associated with the appearance of such a spectral line can be obtained as follows [using Eq. (2–2)]:

$$
\begin{aligned}
2537\ \text{A} &= 2537 \times 10^{-8}\ \text{cm} \\
&= \left(\frac{1}{2537}\right) \times 10^{8}\ \text{cm}^{-1} \\
&= \left(\frac{1}{2537}\right) \times \left(\frac{1}{8076}\right) \times 10^{8}\ \text{eV} \\
&= 4.85\ \text{eV}
\end{aligned}
$$

Thus there is perfect agreement between the optical and electron-collision experiments; both confirm the existence of a discrete electronic excited state of the mercury atom with 4.85 eV more energy than the ground state. Since these early experiments, such **critical excitation potentials** of many atoms have been determined.

Franck and Hertz extended the measurements discussed above by slightly modifying the apparatus, thereby improving the energy resolution. The main decrease in current again occurred at 4.85 eV, but much less-pronounced decreases were observed at other energies noted in Fig. 2–4*b*. Each discontinuity on the curve represents the onset of inelastic collisions between electrons and mercury atoms, and the corresponding energies relate to the energies of various other electronic states of mercury. The ordinary absorption spectrum of mercury vapor does not contain evidence of these other states, which are consequently referred to as "optically forbidden." More correctly, the transitions between the ground state and these excited states are forbidden. The reasons for this forbiddenness will be discussed later. Excited states from which electronic transitions to all lower states are forbidden are known as **metastable states.**

2–4 THE EXCITATION OF SPECTRAL LINES BY ELECTRONIC COLLISIONS

Further confirmation of the inelastic nature of the collisions described above can be obtained by observing the light emission from atoms excited by electron collision. For example, the well-known 2537-A mercury resonance line is observed when mercury is bombarded by electrons of energy greater than 4.85 eV. The normal emission spectrum of mercury vapor consists of many lines in the infrared, visible, and ultraviolet spectral regions. It is pos-

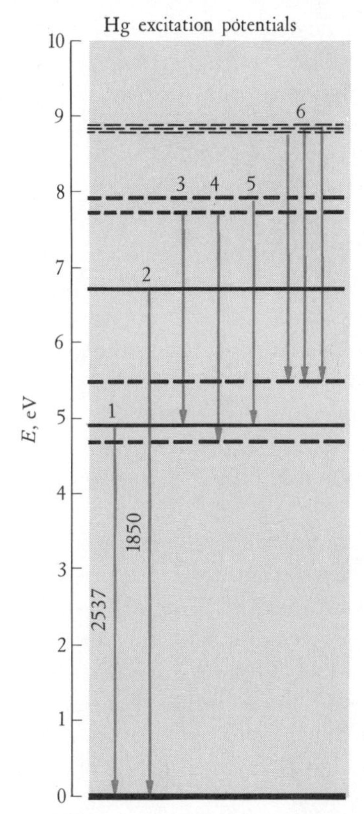

Figure 2–5 **Some of the lower energy states of mercury. The numbers refer to the discussion in the text.**

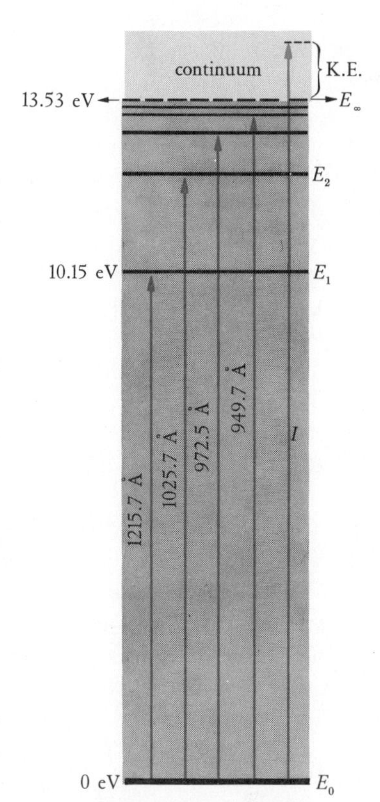

Figure 2–6 **Some of the energy states of the hydrogen Lyman series; the series limit, and continuence states.**

sible to measure the critical excitation potentials for many of these spectral lines. This is done by observing the optical emission spectrum induced by collisions with electrons of different energies.

The results from experiments combining electrical and optical techniques are of tremendous importance in confirming the existence of excited states of atoms. Figure 2–5 shows some of the mercury-atom states drawn on an energy scale referred to the ground state at the zero of energy. The vertical arrows represent certain of the possible transitions (emissions) that can occur. The full horizontal lines represent those states that are not metastable with respect to the ground state. Electrons of 4.85 eV only induce transition number 1, which causes the 2537-A resonance line. As the electron energy is increased, no other lines appear until the energy reaches 6.70 eV, when the 1850-A ultraviolet emission line corresponding to transition 2 becomes detectable. Visible lines 3 and 4, which have a critical potential of 7.73 eV, relate to the 4047-A and 4358-A blue lines. The transition between the ground state and the 7.73-eV state is forbidden. At 7.93 eV the 4078-A line also appears in the emission spectrum (transition 5). When the electron energy reaches 8.83 volts, the near-ultraviolet group of lines at 3663, 3665, and 3656 A are found in the emission spectrum (6).

Although Fig. 2–5 shows only a small number of states of mercury, it should be appreciated that correlations of this nature place the Bohr postulates on extremely solid ground. The fact remains, however, that calculations of the energies of stationary states according to the Bohr picture of the atom do not yield satisfactory results for atoms other than hydrogen. For example, it is far from possible to account for the details of all the states of mercury atoms on this model. The mechanical framework of the Bohr theory fails when there are more than just one electron in the atom. This points to the reason for the failure of the theory—that insufficient account was taken of the interactions between the electrons in the atom. We shall see in the next chapter that further progress could be made only when a new mechanics was devised. The quantum mechanics, as the new mechanics was called, has its own postulates, and in its limit like the Bohr theory, is in correspondence with classical mechanics.

2–5 CONTINUOUS ATOMIC SPECTRA

It has been noted that the atomic spectral series each consist of a set of lines that become closer as the energy of the transition causing the line increases. According to the old empirical theories and the Bohr theory, each series has a theoretical limit—the series limit—at which energy the electron can be considered as being just removed from the discrete atomic states. The emission caused by such electrons dropping back into bound atomic states—or the absorption corresponding to the promotion of electrons from bound atomic states into unbound regions far from the nucleus—is continuous. A continuum of states implies that there is an infinite number of states within any energy region, no matter how small the region.

The simplest example of a series limit and a continuum is the Lyman series of hydrogen in absorption. The lines in the Lyman series correspond to transitions from the ground state of the hydrogen atom to higher states; consequently it is the only hydrogen series that can be observed in absorption experiments with normal hydrogen atoms. The energy-level diagram is shown schematically in Fig. 2–6.

The series limit is given by Eq. (1–9), which for the Lyman series is equal to the Rydberg constant, since $n^2 = 1$. Thus the ionization potential of the normal hydrogen atom is 109,737.31 cm^{-1}, which is equal to 13.53 eV. It is important to see why the series limit corresponds to an ionization potential. An electron excited to a state beyond the series limit has ceased to be bound to the atom. The last, or highest possible, energy state of the atom lies at the series limit; therefore an energy precisely equal to the ionization potential is required to sever the connections between the electron and the atom. Any extra energy given to the electron, e.g., sufficient energy for transition I in Fig. 2–6 to take place, will be utilized as kinetic energy of the departing electron. The excess of energy over 13.53 eV that is imparted to the electron of normal hydrogen will determine the velocity of the photoejected electron.

The limits of the other hydrogen series also correspond to ionization potentials but not to that of the ground state. The Balmer series converges to the limit $R/4$, which gives an ionization potential for the first excited state of hydrogen. The limits $R/9$, $R/16$, etc., give the ionization potentials of the second, third, etc., excited states of hydrogen.

Normally only the series that leads to the ionization energy of the ground state will appear in absorption spectra, but in certain stellar spectra the Balmer series appears in absorption. This interesting occurrence is due to the extremely high temperature of the atmosphere of a star, which causes a considerable portion of the atoms to be in the first excited state (see Plate I).

The appearance of a continuum beyond the series limit of emission spectra is analogously explained. The process of photoionization can be represented by the photochemical equation

$$H + h\nu \rightarrow H^+ + e^-$$

where $h\nu$ (the energy of a photon of frequency ν) represents the photon, H^+ the resulting hydrogen ion, and e^- the ejected electron. The reverse process can take place with equal probability:

$$H^+ + e^- \rightarrow H + h\nu$$

and the result is that light is emitted when the ion captures the electron. If, however, the electrons have kinetic energy, the emission spectrum will be continuous. When the electron being captured has precisely no kinetic energy, it will become bound to the ion, resulting in the production of an atom in its highest-energy bound state; subsequently this excited atom will emit a photon.

The above method is quite general, and has been used to determine the ionization potentials of most atoms. The photoionization technique can be supplemented by electron-impact experiments similar to those previously described. The basic principle underlying the determination of ionization energies by electron impact is detection of the electric current due to the production of positive ions. The electron energy is continuously varied until a current caused by positive ions of the bombarded atoms is just detectable; then the electron energy corresponds to the ionization energy of the atoms. However, ionization energies of atoms can be measured more accurately by photoionization than by electron impact.

The importance of ionization energies in chemistry cannot be overemphasized. This parameter directly gauges the binding energy of the electron in the atom. Much of chemistry is concerned with the relative stability of ions, which is in turn directly related to the energy required to produce these ions from atoms. Furthermore, the subtle fluctuations in the relative ionization potentials of a series of atoms can lead to important deductions regarding the inner electron structure of atoms with many electrons.

2–6 SUMMARY

1. Electrons can acquire kinetic energy of V electron volts if they accelerate through an electrical potential of V volts.

2. One quantum of electromagnetic radiation can cause the ejection of one electron from the surface of a metal. The energy of the radiation is used to overcome the work function W of the metal, and any excess appears as electron kinetic energy. Thus $h\nu = W + \frac{1}{2} mv^2$. [Cf. Eq. (2–4).]

3. During elastic collisions the total kinetic energy does not change. When the internal energy of a particle is changed during a collision, the process is termed inelastic.

4. Ionization potential is the energy required to remove an electron from an atom. It is related to the binding energy of the electron in the atom.

5. The Bohr model for the atom provides for fixed orbits in which electrons can oscillate without radiating. The radiation from atoms arises when electrons make a transition from one orbit to another. Thus spectral lines indicate the difference in energy between two stationary states: $h\nu = E_m - E_n = \Delta E$.

6. Each atom has a continuum of states, which starts at the ionization limit. Photoionization produces electrons with a kinetic energy dependent on the excess of incident energy over the ionization limit.

7. The Franck-Hertz experiment, using the principle of inelastic collisions of electrons with atoms, provides conclusive proof of the existence of excited states of atoms. Refined experiments also detect states which cannot be observed optically thus proving the existence of metastable states of atoms.

8. Further detailed confirmation of the relative energies of atomic states is obtained from experiments on critical excitation potentials. These experiments show unambiguously that the energy of a spectral line is not a measure of the absolute energy of either of the states concerned.

9. Ground- and excited-state ionization potentials can be obtained directly from the series limits of atomic spectra. Absorption spectra provide the ionization potential of the normal atom.

10. The new energy relationships encountered in this chapter were: (*a*) Kinetic energy of a particle of mass m moving with velocity v is $\frac{1}{2}mv^2$. (*b*) Electron energies are given by eV, where e is the electronic charge and V is the potential in volts. The energies are usually expressed in these terms, i.e., in terms of electron volts (eV). The conversion of electron kinetic energies into electromagnetic wave units is obtained as follows:

$$\mathrm{eV} = h\nu = \frac{hc}{\lambda} = hc\bar{\nu}$$

Therefore

$$\mathrm{V} = \left(\frac{hc}{\mathrm{e}}\right)\bar{\nu}$$

Thus

$$\bar{\nu}(\mathrm{cm}^{-1}) = 8068 \text{ volts (eV)} \qquad \text{[cf. Eq. (2–2)]}$$

where

$$h = 6.62 \times 10^{-27} \text{ erg-sec}$$
$$c = 3.0 \times 10^{10} \text{ cm sec}^{-1}$$
$$\mathrm{e} = 1.60 \times 10^{-19} \text{ amp-sec}$$

and

$$1 \text{ volt amp-sec} = 10^7 \text{ erg}$$

III

The Quantum Theory of Atomic Structure

HAVING DISCUSSED particles and their energies in Chap. II, we shall now consider certain relationships between waves and particles that will lead to a qualitative formulation of the quantum theory.

3–1 THE DIFFRACTION OF WAVES

The apparatus of Fig. 3–1 consists of a source of monochromatic light (i.e., light of essentially only one wavelength λ), a lens L to produce a parallel beam of light, and a plate with two small slits S_1 and S_2 through which the light passes to a screen C. If one observes the light pattern on screen C, he will see *a series of illuminated regions*, not the continuously illuminated region that might have been expected. Therefore, under certain conditions *two light beams can enfeeble one another*.

Suppose waves from S_1 and S_2 meet the screen at the point P (Fig. 3–1). Both waves travel at the same velocity and are coherent, i.e., in phase, at the slits. Thus the fluctuating electromagnetic disturbance at P that is due to the wave from S_1 need

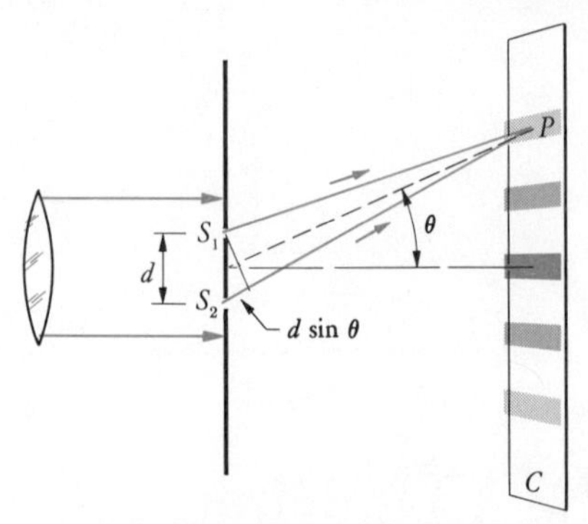

Figure 3–1 A double slit interference experiment.

not be in phase with the disturbance at P that results from the wave from S_2, because the distances S_1P and S_2P are not the same.

If the difference between these two distances is exactly equal to an integral number of wavelengths, the disturbance at P due to the S_1 wave will be exactly duplicated by the S_2 wave; that is, the disturbances will reinforce each other. If the difference in path length is exactly equal to an odd number of half-wavelengths, then the amplitude at P of the S_1 wave will be exactly equal and opposite to the amplitude of the S_2 wave. In this event the two disturbances will exactly cancel each other; no net effect will be experienced at the point P. Clearly there must be many points on the screen for which one or the other of these two conditions are upheld. Consequently the screen will exhibit a pattern of light and dark bands corresponding to the conditions of reinforcement and cancellation of electromagnetic disturbances. The phenomena of reinforcement and cancellation of coherent waves is called **interference.** The consequent arrangement of light and dark bands is called an **interference pattern.**

For two narrow slits that are close together, the difference between path lengths S_1P and S_2P is $d \sin \theta$, where d is the distance between the slits and θ is the angle shown in Fig. 3–1. Thus the conditions for interference are

$$n\lambda = d \sin \theta \qquad \text{reinforcement; brightness}$$
$$(n + \tfrac{1}{2})\lambda = d \sin \theta \qquad \text{cancellation; darkness}$$

where $n = 1, 2, 3, \ldots$, etc. The maximum at $n = 1$ is called the first-order maximum, the maximum at $n = 2$ the second-order maximum, and so on. The most intense peak is first-order. In a one-slit experiment the conditions for darkness and brightness on the screen are reversed, and when $n\lambda = d \sin \theta$ (d is now the width of the slit), a dark band is observed.

A point of maximum brightness for one wavelength will not necessarily be coincident with the point of brightness for any other wavelength, so a device using the interference principle can be used to separate light made up of various wavelengths into its monochromatic components. Such a device is called a **diffraction grating.**[1]

Nature has provided us with a perfect diffracting apparatus for x rays, which are electromagnetic waves with wavelengths of a few Angstrom units. They are beautifully diffracted from the surfaces of crystals. The interatomic spacings in crystals are usually a few Angstroms long, so the atomic layers behave toward x rays like a diffraction grating. Indeed, if we know the wavelength of the x rays from other experiments, we can use the x-ray diffraction pattern to determine the interatomic spacings by applying the formulas given above.

It is to be stressed that the phenomenon of interference can be regarded as a property of waves; conversely a beam that gives a diffraction pattern justifies being represented as a wave motion.

3–2 ANGULAR MOMENTUM

A particle of mass m moving with a velocity v has a linear momentum mv. The velocity of the particle defines both the speed of the particle and the direction in which it is travelling. Thus the linear momentum is a quantity having the direction of v.

---

[1] The phenomena of interference and diffraction are not really different. The resulting patterns of both are caused by the interference of light beams. In interference two coherent beams are brought together after traversing different paths. When a single beam is passed through an aperture, the nature of the diffraction of the beam by the aperture causes self-interference among the many diffracted rays, and a diffraction pattern results. The term diffraction is usually reserved to describe many-beam interference.

When a particle is moving in a circle about a point, it has angular momentum mvr, where r is the distance between the particle and the point. Thus angular momentum is also a directional property, whose direction depends on that of the velocity *and* on that of the line joining the particle to the point about which it is rotating. Therefore, when discussing the angular momentum of a moving particle, *it is necessary to consider spatial orientation.*

If all the forces acting on a particle can be considered as centered at a point around which the particle is rotating, then the angular momentum of the particle is constant in time; i.e., it does not depend on its location in its orbit. The constancy of angular momentum in central field problems of classical mechanics is carried over into the quantum mechanics of the atom. *Angular momentum is a constant of the motion* for an electron in an atom, and each atomic stationary state of this one-electron atom has its own constant angular momentum that describes the state. (The above discussion relates strictly to circular motion of one particle about a fixed point.) The direction of the angular momentum is perpendicular to the plane of rotation but depends on the sense of the rotation. Thus equal and oppositely oriented angular momenta would arise if two particles rotated in opposite directions in the same orbit about the same center.

In the general case of elliptic motion the product of v and r is not constant but depends on r, the distance of the particle from the center. Similar considerations hold for systems involving the motion of many particles as long as there is no interaction between the particles. When there is interaction—as is the case with electrons in an atom—the total angular momentum is still conserved, but the angular momenta of the individual electrons are not constants of the motion. We shall discuss momentum further in Sec. 3–5.

3–3 THE QUANTUM MECHANICS

In the view of Heisenberg (1927) the reason for the failure of the Bohr theory in relation to many-electron atoms was simply that certain precepts within the framework of the theory are physically unrealizable. Certain physical properties are observable in the sense that they can be measured, e.g., the energies and intensities of spectral lines are measurable. The Bohr theory, however, presumes that electrons travel in orbits about the nucleus, and it is physically impossible to observe whether this is the case. To premise a property of matter that is not an observable property must imply, according to Heisenberg, that the premise is invalid.

Why is the motion of an electron in orbit about a nucleus not observable? Suppose the orbit has a diameter of 1 A (10^{-8} cm); for clear observation (presumably with some instrument such as an ultra-high-powered microscope), the wavelength of the radiation employed to observe the object should be less than the size of the object. In other words, radiation of a wavelength about 1 A must be used. But radiation of this wavelength has an energy of

$$10^8 \text{ cm}^{-1} = 1.24 \times 10^4 \text{ eV}$$

which is much greater than the ionization potential of the electron (ca. 10 eV). Consequently the electron is influenced by the radiation to such an extent that it cannot be observed in its unperturbed state. Arguments of this nature lead directly to the conclusion that electrons in stationary atomic states *cannot be ascribed to any particular point or well-defined finite region of space.*

Clearly this last statement conflicts with one of the Bohr postulates, viz., that the electron is constrained to move about the nucleus with definite velocity in a geometrically well-defined orbit. This being so, we must avoid using language of this type to describe the behavior of electrons in atoms, and *the hopeless task of trying to follow electrons in orbits should be abandoned.* We must search for an alternative description consistent with properties of the atom that can be measured experimentally.

The appropriate theory was described by various physicists during the period 1925–1926,[1] and in one form was called wave mechanics, which is founded upon two essential concepts: (1) the wave representation of the electron, and (2) the statistical basis of knowledge.

---

[1] Heisenberg, 1925; Born and Jordan, 1925; de Broglie, 1925; Dirac, 1925; Born, Heisenberg, and Jordan, 1926; Schroedinger, 1926.

We shall now discuss each of these concepts and show how they lead to a unified theory of the behavior of electrons in atoms and molecules.

3–4 THE WAVE REPRESENTATION OF THE ELECTRON

It can be shown mathematically that a moving particle is associable with a wave motion and that the velocity of the moving particle (more correctly the momentum) is inversely proportional to the wavelength of the representative wave motion. The constant of proportionality is Planck's constant, so the **de Broglie relationship** (1924), which expresses this law, is written

$$\text{momentum} = p = \frac{h}{\lambda} \qquad (3\text{–}1)$$

The experimental proof of the wave nature of particles was provided by Davisson and Germer (1927). Their experiment utilized the principle of the diffraction grating.

According to the de Broglie relationship all particles can be regarded as wave motions, and vice versa. The mass or velocity of the particle, and hence its momentum, increases as the wavelength of the representative wave becomes shorter. Thus the long-wavelength ultraviolet radiation can be regarded as a stream of particles of extremely small momentum (photons), and high-energy electrons can be regarded as wave motions of extremely short wavelength. In Davisson and Germer's experiment an electron beam was directed at the surface of crystalline nickel. The reflected beam was analyzed at points corresponding to various angles of reflection, and it was found that the resulting pattern was just what would be expected if the electrons behaved as waves with a wavelength determined by the velocity of the electron beam. For example, with 54-eV electrons the associated wavelength according to the de Broglie relationship is 1.67 A. The first-order maximum of intensity in the reflected electron beam was observed at 50° to a line perpendicular to the crystal surface. Thus from the diffraction formula we have the associated wavelength

$$\lambda = d \sin\theta = 2.15 \text{ A} \times \sin 50° = 1.65 \text{ A}$$

where 2.15 A is the known interatomic spacing in the nickel crystal. The agreement is as nearly perfect as was possible in such an experiment.

3-5 THE STATISTICAL BASIS OF KNOWLEDGE

We have previously seen that the precise location of one electron in an atom is intrinsically uncertain insofar as it is a property that cannot be measured without first disturbing the atomic system. The disturbance really involves the electron acquiring energy during the process of measurement. A more exact statement of what is known as the **Heisenberg uncertainty principle** is that precise measurements of the position and the velocity of an electron cannot be accomplished simultaneously. This means that the position of the electron can be exactly defined only when the velocity (and hence the energy) is completely indeterminate.

Such a principle leads directly to the statistical interpretation of measurements. Each measurement is associated with a definite probability. For example, we could never say that the electron in the hydrogen atom is precisely 0.5 A from the nucleus; we are limited to a knowledge of the *probability* that the electron is 0.5 A from the nucleus. In fact, the most probable place for the electron in the hydrogen atom is precisely at the Bohr radius, but—and this is where Bohr theory and quantum mechanics depart—there also exists a certain probability of finding the electron at every other distance. Of course, the probability of discovering the electron at a long distance from the nucleus is very small. For the hydrogen atom we can obtain what is known as a radial probability-distribution curve, which is a graphic plot of the probability of the electron being within a particular region vs. the distance of that region from the nucleus. The radial curve for the electron in the ground-state hydrogen atom is shown in Fig. 3-2. The dotted vertical line at 0.529 A corresponds to the location of the Bohr orbit. Note that the probability is still relatively large at 1.587 A, which is three times the Bohr radius.

Since calculations yield only probabilities for positions of electrons, it becomes meaningless to form a physical picture of the

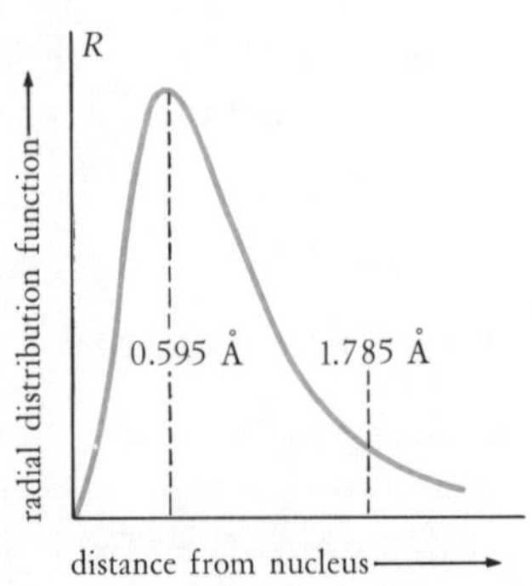

Figure 3–2 Radial distribution curve.

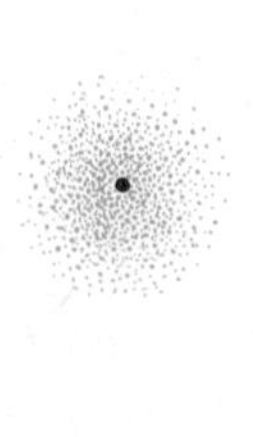

Figure 3–3 Charge cloud representation of an electron in an atom.

atom in which the electron is a clearly defined particle. The statistical nature of our knowledge of atomic structure can be regarded in another way. Suppose we were able to pinpoint the position of the electron in relation to the nucleus in a series of experiments. It would arise that each of our observations would give a different result. Let us now graphically represent these measurements by placing a dot on a diagram to correspond to the position obtained in each experiment. To do this we basically require a three-dimensional figure, but a two-dimensional representation of this is shown in Fig. 3–3. Each dot on the figure corresponds to the result of one experiment. We would find a large concentration of dots near the nucleus. After many experiments the diagram will become almost continuous—corresponding to the idea that, at every position in space, there is some probability of finding the electron.

Such concepts as those expressed in the last few paragraphs lead naturally toward a **charge cloud** as a physical picture for the electrons in atoms. We can proceed further with these ideas and propose a shape for the charge cloud. It would be reasonable to be unconcerned with extremely small probabilities. Suppose we draw a line enclosing all those regions in which the probability of finding the electron is greater than 1 per cent; that is, there is a

99 per cent chance of locating the electron within this boundary. The resulting probability distribution would be spherical.

It is of interest to see how our earlier comments regarding angular momentum relate to the uncertainty principle, since it was stated that the angular momentum can be known precisely for electrons in the hydrogen atom. With reference to the circular orbit, our knowledge of mvr implies a knowledge of the velocity and the radius of the orbit. The position coordinates of the electron depend on r (a constant), and an angular factor that indicates how much rotation has occurred up to the time of measurement. It is the angular factor that is completely indeterminate even when the angular momentum is known precisely. Thus it is not inconsistent with the uncertainty principle to have precise knowledge of angular momenta. For any charge distribution the angular momentum is one parameter that can be exactly defined. It is therefore admissible to retain the angular momentum as a constant of the motion in atomic problems even though the concept of a particle moving in a fixed orbit of radius r and velocity v has been discarded.

With the basic ideas of the wave nature of the electron and the importance of probability in measurement, we are now in a position to proceed with a description of certain results arising from wave mechanical theory which are of primary importance to an understanding of chemistry.

3–6 RESULTS FROM THE WAVE MECHANICAL THEORY OF THE ELECTRON

Once it is confirmed that the electron has wave characteristics, it is not difficult to develop equations to describe the mechanics of atomic systems. The theoretical framework that deals with the equations of motion for waves was well established long before the advent of quantum ideas. Schroedinger (1926) developed a wave equation for the electron, and in so doing he united the classical theory of waves and the de Broglie principle. The results were considered astounding; not only was the hydrogen-atom problem solved exactly, but the helium atom, with two electrons, was well understood soon afterward.

The solutions of the wave equation yielded the explicit mathematical forms for the probability functions mentioned in Sec. 3–5. Besides this, the integral constants of the Ritz-Rydberg formula [Eq. (1–10)] were given the true dynamic significance that had been foreseen by Bohr in the form of a postulate. It is to these constants that we must now direct our attention.

A direct result of wave mechanics is that the energy of an atomic state is dependent on the value of an integral parameter n in the manner of Eq. (3–2).

$$E \propto -\frac{1}{n^2} \qquad \textbf{(3–2)}$$

This equation should be compared with terms in the Ritz combination principle [Eq. (1–10)]. The value of n ($n = 1, 2, 3,$ etc.) controls not only the energy of the atomic state but also the size of the charge cloud of the electron when the atom is in that state. Because of its importance in determining the gross energy and size features of the electron cloud, this integer is called the **principal quantum number.** The radius of the charge cloud is roughly proportional to n^2, which means that for low values of n the energy is low [note the minus sign in Eq. (3–2)] and the charge cloud is small. In other words, the electron is held tightly into the nucleus, giving rise to an energetically stable configuration. Conversely, when the principal quantum number is large, the charge cloud extends further from the nucleus. Thus the excitation of an atom from a lower to a higher state corresponds to the transfer of an electron to a more loosely bound location in the atom.

The atom consists of many well-defined energy regions, each relating to a particular value of n. The electrons are restricted to these numerous energy regions, which for lighter atoms do not overlap. The principal quantum number therefore defines energy **shells** in the atom. The term shell connotes some spatial ordering of electrons with different n values, and this is in accord with the above discussion relating n to the size of the charge distribution. As we shall see below, an electron may lie in one of a variety of subshells, the number and type of which are dependent on n.

At this point it will be useful to reconsider the Bohr theory of the hydrogen atom. According to postulate 2 of Sec. 2–2, only certain discrete electron orbits are permitted. These orbits were assumed to be circular, so the angular momentum of an electron in any stationary state would be constant. Bohr postulated that this constant was $nh/2\pi$, where h is Planck's constant and n is an integer not equal to zero. From the definition of angular momentum (Sec. 3–2), this implies that

$$mvr = nh/2\pi \tag{3-3}$$

If we now write $p = mv$ and combine Eq. (3–3) with Eq. (3–1), we find that

$$p/h = n/2\pi r = 1/\lambda \tag{3-4}$$

where λ is the de Broglie wavelength for particles of momentum p. Rewriting Eq. (3–4) in the form $n\lambda = 2\pi r$ immediately makes clear the significance of the Bohr orbit in wave mechanics. The circumference of a circle of radius r is $2\pi r$; thus Bohr's condition of Eq. (3–3) expresses the fact that the orbits must have their circumferences equal to an integral number of de Broglie wavelengths. In this sense an electron in a Bohr orbit can be represented by a standing wave rather than a progressive wave or moving particle. A standing wave dissipates no energy until acted on by an external force, so we see why the Bohr electron would not continuously radiate, thus collapsing into the nucleus.

In the general case the orbital motion of the electron will be elliptic and not necessarily circular. Bohr and Sommerfeld studied the dynamics of elliptic orbits and concluded that two integers were required to characterize the stationary states. To define elliptic motion we require both the orbital and radial parts of the angular momentum. The former relates to the rate of change of the azimuth of the particle, and the latter to the rate of change of the radius of the orbit. The former quantity is the orbital angular momentum; the latter is the radial momentum.

The solution of the wave equation for the hydrogen atom leads to an orbital quantum number l, which determines the possible values of orbital angular momentum thus:

$$\text{orbital angular momentum} = \sqrt{l(l+1)}\frac{h}{2\pi} \qquad (3\text{–}5)$$

where l takes integral values including zero. In the older Bohr-Sommerfeld theory the possible values of orbital angular momentum were $kh/2\pi$, where k took integral values but not zero. There is no difficulty in visualizing zero orbital angular momentum in a wave mechanical picture; it simply refers to a charge distribution that is not rotating. This concept was not realizable in the classical framework, so k was restricted to integral values.

Broadly speaking, wave mechanical theory has provided the basis for the postulates of Bohr. Atomic energy levels are to be regarded as characterized by special values of the orbital angular momentum. For large values of l the permitted angular momenta are nearly integral multiples of $h/2\pi$[1].

The manner in which the electronic states of hydrogen are constructed on an energy scale depends precisely on the two quantum numbers n and l, described above. The next concept to be discussed is how the various possible values of l are limited by the value of n. The probability functions for each stationary state of the atom depend on the values of n and l; thus for each pair of values (n,l) there is, in the Bohr sense, a stationary state of the atom. The orbital quantum number may take any integral value from 0 through 1, 2, and so on until it is one less than n; that is

$$l = 0, 1, 2, \ldots, (n-1) \qquad (3\text{–}6)$$

Thus the only possible value of l for an electron within the $n = 1$ shell is $l = 0$; within the $n = 2$ shell the orbital quantum number may be 0 or 1; within the $n = 3$ shell, $l = 0$, 1, or 2, and so on.

The energy of a state defined by the quantum numbers (n,l) depends on the value of n and, for atoms other than hydrogen, to a smaller extent on the value of l. For $n = 1$ there is simply one state, (1,0). For $n = 2$ there are two higher-energy states, namely, (2,0) and (2,1). The three states (3,0), (3,1), and (3,2) are next in order of energy.

---

[1] h has the units erg-sec; angular momentum has the units g-cm^2 sec^{-2}; see Problem 4.

There is an arbitrary system currently used for referring to orbital angular-momentum quantum numbers. The letters *s*, *p*, *d*, *f*, *g*, etc., are used to replace the numerical values of $l = 0, 1, 2, 3, 4$, etc. Thus the set (1,0) is called 1*s*; the sets (2,0) and (2,1) are called 2*s* and 2*p*, respectively; the three sets (3,0), (3,1), and (3,2) of the $n = 3$ shell are called 3*s*, 3*p*, and 3*d*, respectively.

Figure 3–4 shows the energy diagram for the states of the hydrogen atom. It should be emphasized that the foregoing discussion of states refers exclusively to hydrogen atoms. When there is more than one electron in the atom, the atomic state is not given simply by quantum numbers for the excited electron. All the electrons in the atom must be considered in order that *a complete atomic-orbital quantum number* can be computed; it is the total orbital angular momentum of the electrons that must be considered.

Figure 3–4 The relative energy of hydrogen atomic orbitals.

The above system of nomenclature is really a system of naming **electron configurations** for hydrogen. Thus hydrogen in its ground state has the electronic configuration $1s^1$, indicating that the electron is representable by a probability-distribution function corresponding to $n = 1$, $l = 0$. In its first excited state the electronic configuration of hydrogen is $2s^1$ or $2p^1$. In its third excited state the configuration is $3s^1$, $3p^1$, or $3d^1$; and so on. When we reexamine the meaning of n and l, we conclude that n determines the average distance of the electron from the nucleus, and the energy of the electron. The orbital quantum number indicates the orbital angular momentum of the electron and hence the shape of the probability distribution. Accepting this, it is seen that the probability distributions for $1s$ and $2s$ are the same shape because they have the same value of l but that $2s$ corresponds to a concentration of electronic charge further from the nucleus because of the larger value of n. All distributions with $l = 0$ are spherically symmetrical about the nucleus. Later in this chapter we shall discuss these and other shapes in detail, but first the above concepts must be extended to include certain new factors arising from the wave mechanical theory.

3–7 ATOMIC ORBITALS

Until now we have regarded the electron cloud and its probability distribution as a principal result of wave mechanics. Actually the wave equation for the atomic system does not include this probability function, but describes the properties of a **wave function** that is closely analogous to a wave amplitude (see Fig. 1–1). As we saw previously, the wave amplitude at any point fluctuates at a certain frequency and measures the magnitude of the disturbance at the point at a given time. The same representation holds true for the wave characteristic of an electron in an atom. It has the property of a fluctuating disturbance, but *the square of this wave characteristic is independent of time* and of course is always a real and positive quantity.

It is this squared amplitude function which is interpreted as the observable probability function that we have been discussing.

Thus fundamentally, the different states of electrons in atoms correspond to the different wave characteristics that the electrons can undertake. As we have seen, only certain definite wave characteristics are possible. The mathematical expressions that exactly define these characteristics are *wave functions.* Since wave functions define the various possible stationary modes in which electrons may reside in atoms (analogous to the orbits of the Bohr theory), these functions are named **atomic orbitals** (cf. *orbital* angular momentum). Thus when we speak of the 1s atomic orbital of hydrogen, we mean the wave characteristic that would be assumed by an electron in the most stable configuration of hydrogen. The function can be accepted as defined by the quantum numbers (1,0) and also by one other factor, which appears in the form of a third quantum number m. Before presenting a detailed discussion of this third quantum number, it should be remarked that we can discuss the "shapes" of wave functions in a manner rather similar to that used to discuss probability distributions. The difference is that wave amplitudes have sign, either positive or negative, since they represent directional disturbances rather than observable probabilities. Thus the s-orbital wave function (usually written as the s orbital) is spherically symmetric about the nucleus. The p orbitals are dumbbell-shaped but the sign of the function is positive in one lobe and negative in the other. In most instances it will be convenient to use the probability distributions for discussion of chemical problems, but, to maintain a certain rigor, the electron configurations of atoms will be introduced from the more fundamental concept of atomic orbitals.

The Magnetic or Orientation Quantum Number

In the previous section nothing was said about the orientation in space of the atomic orbitals. Quantum mechanics tells us that orbital angular momentum of the electron is also quantized in space. This implies that the orbital angular momentum of an electron in an atom can take up only certain directions in space. The results are as follows: For every value of l there corresponds $(2l + 1)$ possible, equivalent spatial orientations. Each of these $(2l + 1)$ quantities is defined by a quantum number m_l, where m_l

takes the $(2l + 1)$ values $\pm l, \pm(l - 1), \pm(l - 2), \ldots, 0$. Thus for s orbitals $(l = 0)$, m_l has only the one value of zero, which signifies the indistinguishability of all possible orientations of a sphere in space. For p orbitals m_l has the three values $(-1,0,+1)$, which signify three possible orientations of the p-type-orbital function in space.[1] Of course each of the three p orbitals has exactly the same energy and is equivalent and essentially indistinguishable under normal conditions. The reason for this is that the atom is not aware of any coordinate system and therefore exhibits no features which distinguish one orientation from the others. However, if the atom is placed in a steady magnetic field or is located in a molecule, the directional interactions that occur along the direction of the field or the chemical bond will force a distinction between the otherwise equivalent p orbitals. In this event the three p orbitals will differ very slightly in energy from one another. The three p orbitals p_x, p_y, and p_z, which are mutually at right angles, form a set of equivalent orbitals (see Fig. 3–5). However the set is not unique in the sense that another set could have been chosen. This particular set is useful in chemical valence problems.[1]

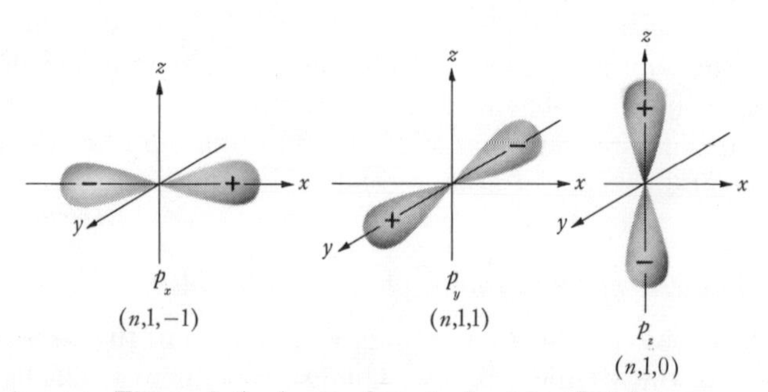

Figure 3–5 A set of equivalent *p* orbitals.

[1] The values of m_l refer to the magnitudes of the projections of the orbital angular momenta onto a given reference axis. The magnitudes are expressed in units of $h/2\pi$. Thus the projections of l onto this axis are (for $l = 1$) $-h/2\pi$, 0, and $h/2\pi$. The set p_x, p_y, and p_z are not proper functions in the sense that the associated angular momenta projections are not ± 1 and 0. However this does not detract from their usefulness in chemical models.

The *d* functions are more complex, and there are five $[(2 \times 2) + 1]$ differently oriented *d* orbitals, some of which are shown in Fig. 3–6. In the labeling of the orbitals in Figs. 3–5 and 3–6 each orientation is designated by three quantum numbers *n*, *l*, and m_l, relating to *size*, *shape*, and *orientation* respectively, and thus defining the major properties of each orbital or electron cloud. In regard to Figs. 3–5 and 3–6 the following should be pointed out:

1. The values of m_l assigned to any particular orbital are arbitrary; there is no energy relationship involved in the numbering system, although the fixed axis is taken to be the *z* axis.

2. The signs on the wave functions (orbitals) have no physical significance; it is only the squares of these functions which represent physically observable quantities.

Radial and Angular Distributions for Atomic Orbitals

It is important to understand fully the relationships between the various types of orbital diagrams that have been presented. To this end we shall rescrutinize the more common representations for charge clouds and orbital functions.

1. The Boundary Surfaces of Orbitals. The surfaces in Figs. 3–5 and 3–6 represent the angular properties of electrons in these orbitals. The distance from the origin to a point on the curve gives the relative probability of finding the electron at any

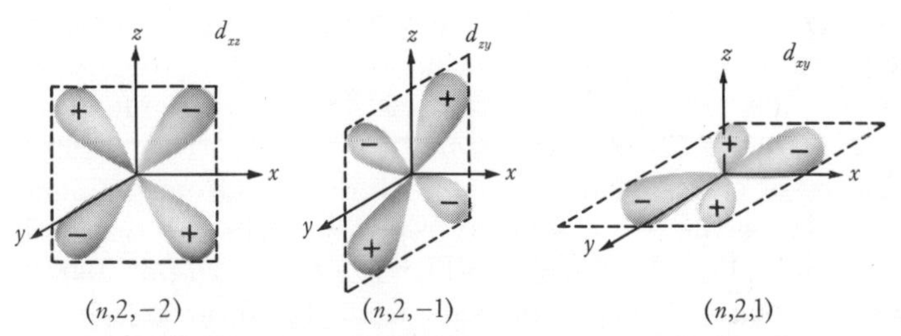

Figure 3–6 Three of the five equivalent *d* orbitals.

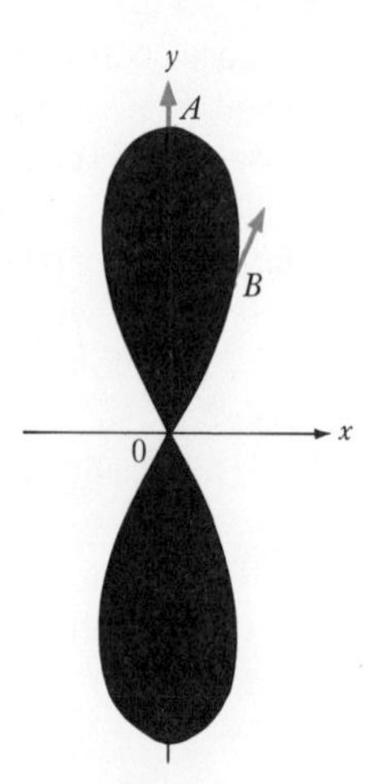

Figure 3–7 Angular probability boundary surface for a *p* orbital.

distance *in that direction.* Thus in Fig. 3–7 the probability of finding the electron in the direction *OA* is roughly twice that of its being located in the direction *OB*. The probability of finding the electron along Ox is exactly zero. For an *s* orbital the angular distribution is represented by a spherical surface, and the electron has equal probabilities for all directions. These angular properties do not depend on the value of the principal quantum number. *They indicate nothing regarding the variation of the probability with the distance of the electron from the nucleus.* Figures 3–5 and 3–6 are representations of the angular properties of the wave function; equivalent diagrams such as Fig. 3–7 represent the angular properties of the probability. The latter type are obtained from the former by squaring the value of the orbital function at each point in space.

2. The Radial Distribution. This is used to indicate the variation of charge-cloud density with distance from the nucleus. Radial properties are commonly represented in two ways. The first is exemplified by Fig. 3–2, which is a plot of **radial distribution function** R against distance from the nucleus. The value of R at any distance r from the nucleus indicates the probability

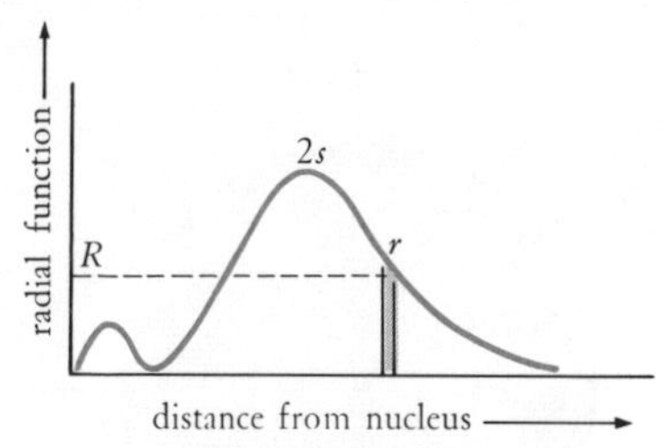

Figure 3–8 The radial distribution function for a 2s orbital.

of finding the electron inside a thin spherical shell of radius r. Thus in Fig. 3–8 the probability of finding the electron in a thin shell (the thickness of the shell should be infinitesimal, but is represented by two closely spaced lines) of radius r, is given by R. The radial distribution of Fig. 3–8 is for a 2*s* orbital.

The **radial density distribution** shown in Fig. 3–9 is an alternative method of depicting radial probabilities. In this case the electron density (the probability of finding an electron in unit volume) is plotted against the distance from the nucleus. Figure

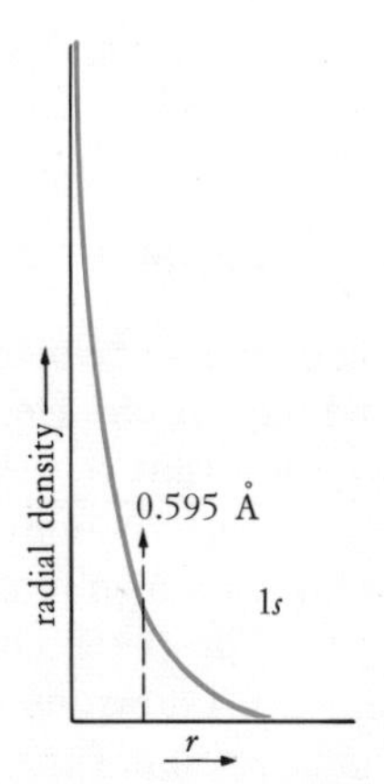

Figure 3–9 The radial density distribution for a 1s orbital.

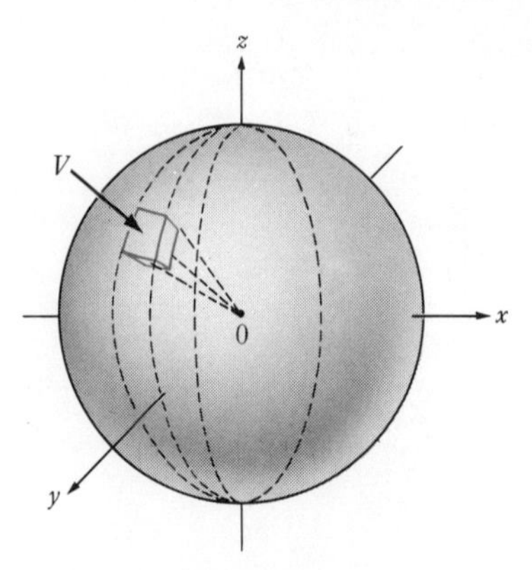

Figure 3–10 Diagram illustrating the meaning of radial density.

3–9, for a 1*s* orbital, should be carefully compared with Fig. 3–2, since both diagrams represent the same distribution. The physical meaning of radial density is again illustrated in Fig. 3–10. The probability of finding the electron within the small unit volume *v* is the radial density along the direction 0V.

The charge-cloud description attempts to unite an angular boundary surface and a radial density distribution. To see this the student should compare Figs. 3–3 and 3–9.

3–8 ELECTRON SPIN

By introducing the concepts of relativity into the wave equation, Dirac (1928) showed that each electron in the atom has an angular momentum other than that resulting from its orbital motion. This new quantity can be thought of as derived from the rotation of the electron about its own axis. It is this momentum that gives rise to the magnetic properties of materials. The fourth (and last) quantum number *s*, known as the spin quantum number, is reserved for characterization of the component spin angular momentum along a given reference axis. There are only two possible values for the spin angular momentum quantum number of an electron: The value of s can be either plus or minus one-half.

$$s = \pm\tfrac{1}{2}$$

Note that s is the quantum number for spin angular momentum and is not the angular momentum. The components of the spin angular momentum are $\pm\frac{1}{2}(h/2\pi)$, corresponding to positive and negative directions of the fixed axis. The spin angular momentum (*not* the component) is given by $\sqrt{s(s+1)}(h/2\pi)$, where s is the absolute magnitude of the spin quantum number, which is equal to $\frac{1}{2}$.

Now we can exactly define the nature of an electron in the hydrogen atom by means of four numbers (n,l,m_l,s). The spin does not affect the energy to any appreciable extent, so the lowest-energy complete configuration of hydrogen may be written either as $(1,0,0,+\frac{1}{2})$ or $(1,0,0,-\frac{1}{2})$. What we had previously considered as a single state corresponds to two states coincident in energy. Clearly we require a more precise definition for atomic states and configurations. The matter of states we defer until Chap. V. We shall define a configuration as specifying (n,l) for every electron in the atom and leave the matter of orientation (m_l) and spin (s) until later.

In review we concluded that the classical theory of electron dynamics failed to account for the spectral lines obtained from atoms because accelerating charges should radiate, according to classical theory. The Bohr theory overcame this difficulty by the postulation of discrete orbits for which classical dynamics is valid except for the ability of electrons to remain in these orbits without radiating. The observed spectral lines were then interpreted as arising from quantum transitions of electrons between the fixed orbits. Because of the uncertainty principle certain difficulties arose in confining the electronic motion to a fixed line. These difficulties were removed by reconsidering the electron in the atom as a super-position of interfering waves. The characteristics of the wave motion of the electron in an atom were obtainable from wave mechanics, and the one-electron atom under discussion was then treated in terms of probability functions. The results of wave mechanics led to the three spatial quantum numbers n, l, and m_l, which label the energies, shapes, and orientations of the various permitted charge distributions. Finally the electron spin quantum number was introduced, thus completing the set (m,l,m_l,s) of quantities required for the characterization of the states of an atom. Throughout this development the concept of conservation of angular momentum was stressed even though the angular momentum of a charge distribution has little obvious classical significance. The previous discussion referred principally to one-electron atoms.

3–9 SUMMARY

1. The electron can be ascribed the properties of both a particle and a wave. The particle property (momentum p) and wave property (wavelength λ) are related through Planck's constant by the de Broglie equation $p = h/\lambda$.

2. The Heisenberg uncertainty principle indicates that the position and the velocity of the electron cannot both be simultaneously and precisely measured. Thus follows the intrinsic statistical basis of our knowledge of events at the atomic level.

3. The solution of the wave equation for the hydrogen atom provides us with the concept of atomic orbitals (or atomic wave functions), which relate to the probable distribution of electric charge about the nucleus for the various states of the atom.

4. The emergence from wave mechanics of four quantum numbers enables us to define the nature of (*a*) the size and energy of the charge distribution, and shell structure (principal quantum number $n = 1, 2, 3, \ldots$, etc.), (*b*) the shape of the charge distribution [orbital quantum number $l = 0, 1, 2, \ldots, (n-1)$]; (*c*) the orientation of the orbital or charge cloud in space [magnetic quantum number $m_l = \pm l, \pm(l-1), \pm(l-2), \ldots, 0$]; and (*d*) the spin of the electron, which gives rise to its magnetic moment (spin quantum number $s = \pm\frac{1}{2}$). The latter two quantum numbers m_l and s refer to the projections of the orbital and spin angular momenta onto a fixed reference axis. These numbers are observable quantities.

5. An electron in atomic hydrogen is completely defined by the quantum numbers (n,l,m_l,s), but each atomic configuration is in

reality two states because of the two possible (and indistinguishable) values of s.

6. The notation adopted for the description of atomic orbitals is to replace values of $l = 0, 1, 2$, etc., by the lowercase letters s, p, d, etc. The shell number, or principal quantum number, is placed before the orbital quantum number. Thus, the orbital with $n = 1, l = 0$ is written as $1s$, whereas $n = 3, l = 2$ is written as $3d$.

7. To distinguish the p orbitals having different orientations the rectangular coordinate (x, y, or z) along which the orbital is directed is subscripted. There are three p orbitals in every shell (for every n), viz., p_x, p_y, and p_z. These are indistinguishable, and equivalent in the absence of a directing field.

8. In an atom that has any number of electrons we have knowledge of the electron configuration if we know (n,l) for every electron.

PROBLEMS

1. Show that the kinetic energy of an electron is proportional to the square of its momentum ($E = p^2/2m$).

2. Calculate the wavelength of the second-order maximum in the Davisson-Germer experiment.

3. In Eq. (3–2) the energy is related to the square of the principal quantum number. Show that under certain conditions the momentum is directly proportional to the principal quantum number. *Hint:* see Problem 1.

4. Prove that Planck's constant has the units of angular momentum.

5. Calculate the orbital angular momentum of a bound electron in units of $h/2\pi$ for values of $l = 0, 1, 2, 3$, and 10, and compare the results with those obtained from the simpler Bohr formula.

6. Explain why the radial density and radial distribution curves are not the same. (*Hint:* read over the definitions carefully and note that the volume of a spherical shell depends on the distance of the shell from the nucleus, whereas the volume element in Fig. 3–10 does not depend on r.)

7. Distinguish carefully between a state and a configuration, as the terms are used in this chapter.

IV

The Pauli Principle and the Electronic Structure of Atoms

AT PRESENT WE HAVE LEARNED that an electron in an atom can be characterized by four quantum numbers (n,l,m_l,s). What we do not know, however, is how many electrons can have a particular set of quantum numbers. This question is answered immediately by the **Pauli exclusion principle** (1926), which states that each electron is characterized by a *unique set of four quantum numbers:* Alternatively, no two electrons in the same atom can have the same set of quantum numbers (n,l,m_l,s). The Pauli principle has a variety of consequences which are of incomparable importance to chemistry.

4-1 THE OCCUPATION OF ATOMIC ORBITALS BY ELECTRONS

When the Pauli principle is applied to the shell with principal quantum number $n = 1$, we see that the following sets of quantum numbers are permissible: $n = 1$, $l = 0$, $m_l = 0$, and either $s = +\frac{1}{2}$ or $s = -\frac{1}{2}$; that is, the two possible sets of quantum numbers for $n = 1$ are $(1,0,0,+\frac{1}{2})$ and $(1,0,0,-\frac{1}{2})$. Thus in any atom only two electrons can occupy a 1*s* orbital; these electrons will differ only in their spin quantum numbers. Since the spin quantum numbers have different signs the total spin angular momentum quantum number is zero $(+\frac{1}{2} - \frac{1}{2} = 0)$. The two electrons are said to be *paired.* It would not be possible to have two electrons whose spins were unpaired in a 1*s* orbital, otherwise they would require the same set of four quantum numbers.

Turning now to the $n = 2$ shell, the possible values of l are 0 and 1 (*s* and *p*). For $l = 0$ only one m_l value is possible ($m_l = 0$) so by the same reasoning as above only two electrons may occupy the 2*s* orbital. They are paired, and have quantum numbers $(2,0,0,\pm\frac{1}{2})$. Since m_l can take the three values $(-1,0,+1)$ for $l = 1$, there are a total of six electrons with $l = 1$, whose quantum numbers are derived as shown in Table 4–1. To obtain the quantum number of, say, the fourth electron, we note that it has $m_l = 0$ corresponding to $l = 1$, with $n = 2$; thus it is $(2,1,0,-\frac{1}{2})$. The principal quantum number defines a shell of the atom, and analogously the orbital quantum number l defines a subshell. The set of quantum numbers above, derived from $l = 1$, define the 2*p* subshell.

Table 4–1

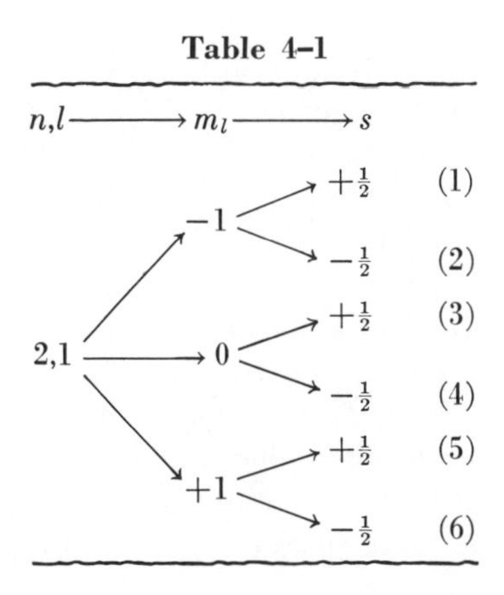

The student will see that certain regularities can already be predicted. He will see, for example, that an *ns* orbital can have only two electrons regardless of the value of n. The two electrons will have quantum numbers $(n,0,0,+\frac{1}{2})$ and $(n,0,0,-\frac{1}{2})$. Analogously the *np* subshell can always provide for six electrons regardless of the value of n (of course n must be at least equal to 2 before the possibility of a *p* subshell arises).

In the previous chapter we found that the orbital motion of the electron is defined by only three (spatial) quantum numbers (n,l,m_l), whereas the fourth quantum number (s) defines the spin. Accordingly we can define the atomic orbitals in terms of n, l, and m_l. Thus the number of possible m_l values for a given l tells us immediately the number of atomic orbitals of that type. There is only one *s* orbital in each shell. Each *s* orbital can accommodate only two electrons whose spins must be paired. Suppose now that $l = 2$ (for this it would be necessary that n was at least 3) and let us obtain the number of *d* orbitals. The possible values of m are -2, -1, 0, 1, and 2; that is, there are five different values that provide for precisely five *d* orbitals. Each orbital can accommodate two electrons $(s = \pm\frac{1}{2})$ so there can be a maximum of ten electrons within the *d* subshell. For $l = 3$ (*f* subshell) the possible values for m_l are -3, -2, -1, 0, 1, 2, and 3. These seven values designate the seven possible *f* orbitals each of which can be occupied by two electrons thus providing for a maximum of 14 electrons in the *f* subshell. Note that the number of orbitals in a subshell of given l is $(2l + 1)$.

Now we are in a position to return to the arrangement of subshells within the shells. When $n = 2$ there can be two electrons in the 2*s* orbital and six electrons in the 2*p* subshell. Since $l = 0$ and $l = 1$ cover all possible values of l for $n = 2$, there can be a maximum of eight electrons in the $n = 2$ shell. The total number of electrons that may occupy the $n = 3$ shell is eighteen, obtained by adding *two* for 3*s*, *six* for 3*p*, and *ten* for 3*d*.

Figure 3–4 showed the relative energies of the various shells and subshells of the hydrogen atom. Notice that the levels become closer together as the value of n increases (cf. the convergence of spectral series into a continuum). Notice also that three lines (levels) at the same energy are used to represent the three equivalent p-orbital energies, and five lines at one energy depict each set of five equivalent d orbitals.

The next step in our description of the electronic structure of atoms will be to discover the detailed electron configuration for various atoms. This should not be difficult, since it is already known how many orbitals are available, how many electrons can be accommodated in each of these orbitals, and the relative energies of the orbitals. We shall first review another physical principle that relates the binding energy of an electron to its relative stability in the atom.

There are two usual ways of defining zero energy: (1) when the electron is at rest, an infinite distance from the nucleus; and (2) when the atom is in its ground state. The location of the zero of energy is arbitrary and the notions (1) and (2) simply correspond to two different scales. However they are each useful in discussing the energetics of atoms and electrons.

When an electron is in the $n = 1$ shell it is, on the average, close to the nucleus. Its binding energy is large in relation to that of an electron which is more distant. To remove an electron from an atom will require the addition of an amount of energy exactly equal to the binding energy of the electron. When the electron is recaptured by the positive ion, the binding energy is released in some form, e.g., as light. The energy is defined as being zero when the electron is at rest and is removed to an infinite distance from the atom. As the electron approaches the nucleus the potential energy increases numerically toward a large negative number. However the value (i.e., the algebraic value) of the potential energy decreases as the force exerted on the electron by the nucleus increases. Thus electrons in orbitals having high negative binding energy are termed stable, since more energy is required to separate them from the atom. When orbitals are placed on an energy scale, the most stable orbital is usually placed at the bottom of the diagram. It has become current usage to associate a low energy orbital with stability but it is always safest to define exactly which energy scale is inferred.

An atom in its ground state has its electrons in the orbitals of maximum possible binding energy. Thus as previously mentioned, the lowest state of hydrogen consists of an electron in the 1s orbital.

The lowest-energy electron configuration of helium, which has two electrons, has both of the electrons in the 1*s* orbital. Such a configuration is written $1s^2$, where the superscript indicates the number of electrons in the orbital. In this case it is not necessary to include the spins in the description because we know that the two electron spins must be paired. The next most stable configuration for the helium atom has one electron in the 1*s* orbital and the other electron in the 2*s* orbital and is written as $1s^12s^1$. For the $1s^12s^1$ configuration it becomes necessary to stipulate the over-all spin because the Pauli principle no longer requires the spins to be paired. Thus the total spin may be either 0 $(+\frac{1}{2} - \frac{1}{2})$ or 1 $(+\frac{1}{2} + \frac{1}{2})$, which means that this *single configuration*, (He)$1s^12s^1$, corresponds to *two atomic states* differing in total spin. These aspects will be treated more fully in the next chapter.

The most stable electron configuration for lithium, which has three electrons, is that with two electrons in the 1*s* orbital, and the third electron in the 2*s* orbital—namely, $1s^22s^1$. The normal configuration of beryllium with four electrons is $1s^22s^2$.

Once it becomes necessary to use the atomic *p* orbitals we are faced with a further difficulty. Let us consider the carbon atom with its six electrons. Following the above arguments it is clear that the lowest-energy configuration is $1s^22s^22p^2$. However in this description the placement of the last two electrons in the 2*p* subshell requires some specification of which of the equivalent *p* orbitals are actually occupied. There are three *p* orbitals p_x, p_y, and p_z each capable of accommodating two electrons. Some of the various possible arrangements of the two electrons among the three orbitals are represented in Fig. 4–1. Electrons with spin

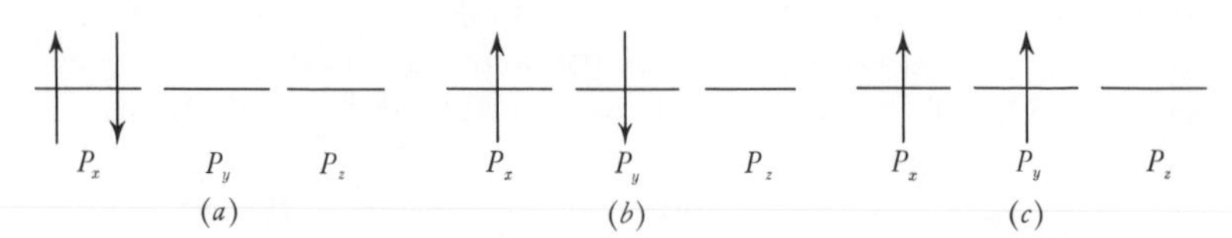

Figure 4–1 Possible arrangements of electrons in the p^2 configuration.

projections $+\frac{1}{2}$ and $-\frac{1}{2}$ are conventionally written as $\uparrow$ and $\downarrow$, respectively.

It should be recalled that the observable atomic quantities do not include the detailed positions of electrons but only the energies of resulting electronic states of the atom, and the *total* angular momentum. Correspondingly it is true that *we are unable to distinguish one electron from another.* In other words, the configuration in which the first electron is in p_x and the second in p_y is indistinguishable from the configuration in which the second electron is in p_x and the first is in p_y. Since we cannot distinguish p_x from p_y or p_z under normal conditions, the configurations in Fig. 4–1 are representative of all the possible p^2 configurations.

The relative energies of the three possible p^2 configurations can be obtained by following **Hund's rule of maximum multiplicity.** This rule states that the most stable electron configuration within a given subshell is that with the maximum number of unpaired electrons in accordance with the Pauli principle. By this token configuration (*c*) in Fig. 4–1 is the lowest energy one. It is readily seen why configuration (*a*) is not preferred if one remembers that the electrons in an atom repel one another. The p_x and p_y orbitals are in different regions of space; thus in configuration (*c*) the electrons are on average further apart than they would be in (*a*) where they are both in the same region of space. Since the repulsion energy detracts from the binding energy the most stable configuration is that with the electrons furthest apart. For our discussions of the most stable electron configurations of atoms it will not be necessary to consider those of the type (*b*) with unpaired electrons of different spin in different orbitals of a subshell.

Electrostatic Repulsion Energies

The remarks above may require some further justification. Hund's rule has its ultimate basis in **Coulomb's law,** which states that like charges repel one another with a force inversely proportional to the square of their separation. The energies associated with such forces are known as repulsion energies, and they add positive contributions to the negative energy of the atom. Thus an increase of repulsion energy causes a decrease in total electron binding energy. It is precisely this factor that causes the orbital structure of many-electron atoms to differ from that of the hydrogen atom. In fact only if the repulsion energies within the shells remain smaller than the principal-quantum-number energies is there any justification in retaining the hydrogenic-shell description for many-electron atoms. These comments are important for the further discussion of screening in Sec. 4–2, and the origin of terms from configurations in Sec. 5–1. If the above were not the case and the electron repulsion dominated, we would not be able to predict the shell structure that is inferred from experimental chemical periodicity.

For the p subshell we encounter a spatial degeneracy, that is, the energy of the three p orbitals are identical; consequently the correct description of an atom is usually not provided by a single configuration. Later (p. 79) we shall see that the correct descriptions are provided by *terms* and *levels* which are superpositions of electron configurations. For example in Fig. 4–1a the configurations $p_x^0 p_y^2 p_z^0$ and $p_x^0 p_y^0 p_z^2$ are equally probable in one of the terms which arise from the p^2 configuration. (The term is ^1S; see p. 94.) In this case the charge distribution is spherically symmetric.

It is not difficult to extend this notion of spatial degeneracy to the other possible configurations for p^2. The properly described components of the p^2 configuration that involve configurations like 4–1b and 4–1c consist of superpositions of these configurations, but p_x, p_y, and p_z do not necessarily occur with equal weights. For example one of the components (^1D, $M_L = 1$; see p. 95) consists of a superposition of the configurations $p_x^1 p_y^0 p_z^1$ and $p_x^0 p_y^1 p_z^1$; this means that the charge densities in p_x, p_y, and p_z are in the ratio 1:1:2. Accordingly, the charge distribution of the atom in this state is not sperically symmetric.

These considerations of spatial degeneracy lead to the conclusion that, if we wish to build realizable configurations, we cannot simply choose the sets (a), (b), or (c). We shall see in Sec. 5–1 that the proper sets of configurations belonging to a particular energy are called terms. The words "realizable" and "proper" are used here to emphasize the point that we have no method of examining detailed configurations of the types mentioned. We can only say something about the terms arising from these configurations and about the relative energies of terms as evidenced from electron repulsion energies.

In terms of electron waves the above statements imply that the actual stationary states of the complex atom involve superpositions of wave functions corresponding to single detailed configurations. In hydrogen the energies are independent of l and m_l, whereas in complex atoms the energy depends on l for each electron. It is important to realize that the orbitals of complex atoms are derived from hydrogen-like orbitals.

4–2 THE ELECTRONIC STRUCTURE OF ATOMS AND THE PERIODIC TABLE

The shell structure that restricts the electronic motions in atoms arises because of the Pauli principle. As far as we know, this basic shell structure is maintained in all atoms regardless of the number of electrons in the atom. Thus by utilizing the concepts developed in the previous section, it should be possible to construct the electronic configuration for any atom solely from the knowledge of the number of electrons in that atom.

The number of electrons in an atom is of course a quantity that is known from other physicochemical studies. The **atomic number** refers to the number of protons in the nucleus, which *for a neutral atom* exactly equals the number of electrons. In the **periodic table of elements** the various atoms are listed horizontally in order of increasing atomic number. A new row is started for each new shell. Thus the first row consists of only two atoms H and He with electronic structures $1s^1$ and $1s^2$, respectively. The next row, corresponding to the $n = 2$ shell, contains the eight new atoms of atomic number 3 to 10, since a maximum of eight electrons can be accommodated in the $n = 2$ shell. If the atomic orbitals for every atom were in the same energy sequence as those of the hydrogen atom, the construction of the periodic table would be rather simple. However this is not the case, and the lower-energy orbitals of many-electron atoms usually follow the apparently unusual energy sequence $1s < 2s < 2p < 3s < 3p < 4s < 3d < 4p < 5s < 4d < 5p < 6s < 4f$. The order of stability

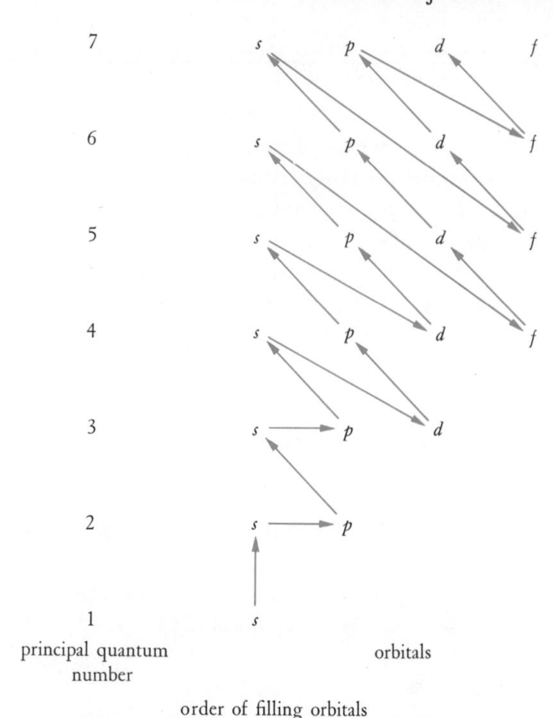

Figure 4–2 The order of filling orbitals.

of the orbital does not necessarily fall in line with the value of the principal quantum number (see Fig. 4–2). For example 4*s* is often more stable than 3*d*; 5*s* can be at lower energy than 4*d*; and 4*f* is less stable than either 5*s*, 5*p*, or 6*s*. *These apparent anomalies have a genuinely profound effect on chemical periodicity, and their origin is based on the fact that we have neglected to consider the influence of the filled inner shells on the electrons in outer orbitals.* That is, no electron repulsion is included in the derivation of the hydrogenic orbitals.

Screening Effects of Inner-shell-electron Clouds

Let us compare the influence of the nuclear charge on a single 3*d* or 4*s* electron in an atom of atomic number 19, with the effect of the hydrogen nucleus on the hydrogen electron in a $3d$ or $4s$ orbital. A $3d$ electron of hydrogen has a charge cloud that is closer to the nucleus than the charge cloud of the $4s$ electron. Because of the nature of the probability distribution for the two orbitals (shown in Fig. 4–3), a good comparison of the energies can be obtained by comparing the distances from the nucleus of the peaks of the $3d$ and $4s$ probability distributions. Clearly the peak of the $3d$-orbital distribution is closest to the nucleus, so it is a more stable orbital. The small probability of the $4s$ electron being close to the nucleus, and the much smaller probability of the $3d$ electron being extremely close to the nucleus (these regions are represented by dashed lines in Fig. 4–3), are not so important in determining the relative energies of the orbitals because the electron is most often far from the nucleus.

For the atom with 19 electrons (potassium) the nuclear charge is $+19$ and the configuration for the first 18 electrons is unambiguously $1s^2 2s^2 2p^6 3s^2 3p^6$. Since this is the electronic configuration of the neon atom we can abbreviate these symbols to [Ne]. Thus potassium has either the electronic configuration [Ne]$4s^1$ or [Ne]$3d^1$. The latter configuration would be the most acceptable provided we employed the same reasoning that was used for the hydrogen atom. This, however, would be incorrect because the 18 inner-shell electrons, which are tightly bound to the nucleus, *effectively screen the outer electron from the nuclear charge.* The *effective* nuclear

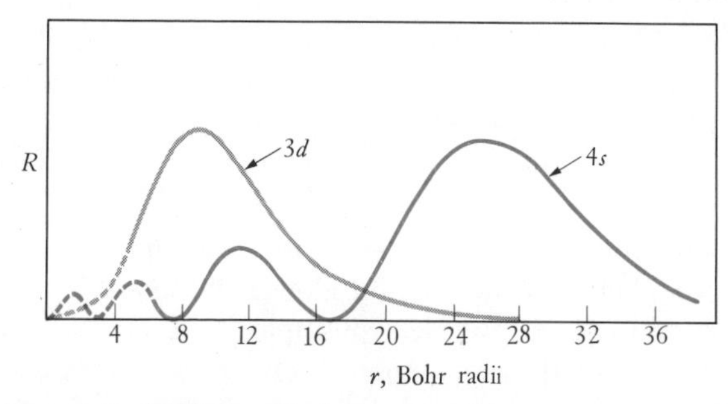

Figure 4–3 Radial probability distributions for hydrogen $4s$ and $3d$ orbitals.

charge experienced by the outer electron is less than the *true* nuclear charge because of a screening by the charge clouds of the inner, tightly bound electrons. We can see from Fig. 4–3 that of the two distributions the $4s$ will penetrate this screen most effectively, owing to the larger value of the $4s$ probability close to the nucleus. For this reason the $4s$ orbital of potassium is slightly more stable than the $3d$ orbital. The lowest energy configuration of potassium is therefore [Ne]$4s^1$. The next atom in order of atomic number is calcium (20), which has the configuration [Ne]$4s^2$.

As we shall see later, screening is also important in describing the sizes and ionization potentials of atoms. The important result for the present is that, in general, the ns orbital will be filled before the $(n-1)d$ orbitals. This is a direct consequence of the greater stability of the s orbitals compared with the $(n-1)d$ set in most neutral atoms. It is of the utmost importance to realize that the above discussion refers to *neutral atoms*, not to ions with the same number of electrons. For example, K and Sc^{2+} have equal numbers of electrons yet they do not have the same electron configuration. The reason for this will be explained later (see Problem 7).

4–3 THE STABILITY OF FILLED AND HALF-FILLED SUBSHELLS

The stability or instability of the atom is determined by the total binding energy for the system of electrons moving in complex motions about a positively charged nucleus. The electrons are each attracted to the nucleus so a portion of the total binding energy is determined by this electron-nuclear attraction. This part of the total binding energy is greatest when the electrons are closest to the nucleus. Consequently, for a given number of electrons, the greatest stability will be achieved by having the atom as small as possible.

The electrons, however, interact with one another and the repulsive forces between them tend to lower the total binding energy (i.e., they tend to force the electrons apart and increase the size of the atom). Hence the most stable configuration of an atom must represent *a compromise between the electron-nuclear attractive forces and the electron-electron repulsive forces.* The first (or lowest) ionization potential of an atom is a direct measure of the binding energy of the least tightly bound electron in the atom. Hence it is a measure of stability, as the term is used here, since the remaining electrons are each more tightly bound than the one that was first removed during ionization. We know that the electronic configurations of H, He, and Li are, respectively, $1s^1$, $1s^2$, and $1s^2 2s^1$. Experimentally it is found that the ionization potentials of these atoms are 13.595, 24.58, and 5.39 eV, respectively. Let us see whether we can explain these values on the basis of the known atomic structures.

Hydrogen should certainly have a lower ionization potential than helium because each electron in helium is attracted to a nucleus with two positive charges, whereas the hydrogen electron is held by only one positive charge. However, to offset this, the electrons in helium repel one another appreciably, since they tend to be in the same region of space (i.e., in a $1s$ orbital). Consequently the ionization potential of helium is less than twice that of hydrogen, the deviation being accounted for by electron-electron repulsion of the helium electrons. Lithium has a nuclear charge of $+3$ units, so that the two $1s$ electrons in lithium are bound even more tightly than they are in helium (see Fig. 4–4). However, according to the Pauli principle the third electron must go into a $2s$ orbital, which restricts this electron to a more distant location from the nucleus. What the Pauli principle is asserting here is that the third electron tends to avoid the $1s^2$ pair of electrons. We reach the same conclusion by applying the Hund rule in the form that electrons with the same spin tend to stay apart. The third electron in lithium, regardless of its spin, will tend to avoid the electron pair because it must have the same spin as one of the electrons in the pair. Tendencies of this nature manifest themselves as contributions to the total binding energy. Thus the fact that the third, or outer, electron of lithium is forced to be distant from the $1s^2$ pair, and hence from the nucleus, means that it is very much less tightly bound to the nucleus, and is consequently the most readily ionizable. A further conclusion to be drawn from this discussion is that an unusually high stability can be expected *whenever the outermost electrons in an atom are in a filled shell or filled subshell.* On the

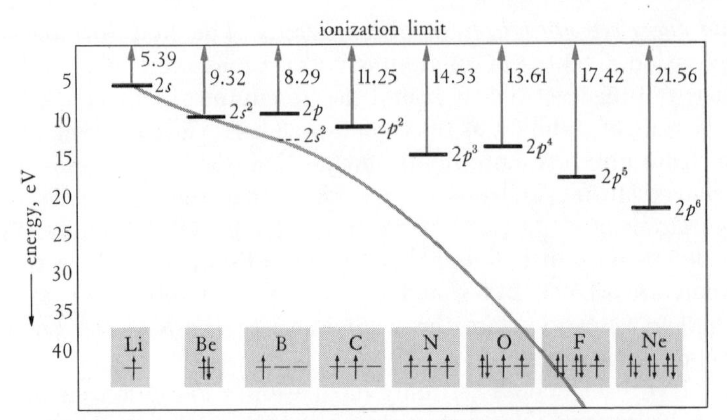

Figure 4–4 The relative stability of highest occupied orbitals for atoms in the first row of the periodic table. The vertical arrows are the ground-state ionization potentials. The curve shows the approximate energies of the valence-shell $2s^2$ electrons.

one hand the binding energy of the electron in a filled shell is much higher than that of the outermost electron in the next atom; e.g., the ionization potential of He is much greater than that of lithium. On the other hand, the larger nuclear charge of the filled-shell atom compared with the nuclear charge of the previous atom results in an increase in ionization potential.

It follows that the series of atoms with atomic numbers 2, 10, 18, 36, 54, etc., corresponding to those whose outermost electrons belong to a filled shell with principal quantum numbers 1, 2, 3, 4, 5, etc., will have the largest possible ionization potentials for electrons in each of these shells. This group of atoms, the rare gases He, Ne, A, Kr, Xe, represent some of the least chemically reactive elements.

Just as unusual stability results from a filled shell or subshell, so it does for half-filled subshells. In this case the Hund rule applies directly, and relative stability arises because a half-filled subshell contains the maximum possible number of unpaired electrons (minimum electron repulsion). Thus nitrogen ($1s^22s^22p^3$) with a half-filled $2p$ subshell has a higher ionization potential than oxygen ($1s^22s^22p^4$) despite the larger nuclear charge on oxygen. The structures of the $2p$ subshells for these atoms are shown in Fig. 4–4 together with the ionization energies and electron configurations of the elements from Li to Na. In this diagram the inner shell has been omitted, since electrons in the $1s$ orbitals are very tightly bound in these atoms. The horizontal line at the top of the diagram is the ionization limit, and the individual horizontal levels represent the energies of the atomic ground states. Thus the length of the vertical line from the uppermost level to the ionization limit corresponds to the ionization energy of the outermost electron. The ionization potential will normally increase with increasing nuclear charge, but notice how that of Be($1s^22s^2$, filled subshell) is higher than B($1s^22s^22p^1$); and that N($1s^22s^22p^3$, half-filled subshell) is higher than O($1s^22s^22p^4$); and that Ne($1s^22s^22p^6$, filled subshell) is higher than Na($1s^22s^22p^63s^1$).

The Periodic Table

The aim of a periodic classification of elements is to provide a logical arrangement of elements such that trends and similarities in the chemical and physical properties of atoms become apparent from the nature of the ordering. In this sense chemical periodicity was realized many years before quantum theory. The wave mechanical theory of atoms provides the logic behind the periodic classification. The link between the chemical and the theoretical classifications depends on the fact that *elements with similar electronic configurations may be expected to have similar chemical and physical properties.*

Before we proceed to build up the electronic structures of the remaining groups of atoms in the periodic table, the various principles involved in this process will be summarized.

1. The features that distinguish one atom from another are the nuclear charge and the number of electrons. For neutral atoms these are equal.

2. The motion of each electron in an atom is characterized by a wave function relating to a particular distribution within its charge cloud.

3. Each set of quantum numbers (n,l,m_l) defines a particular wave function, or atomic orbital, which describes the energy, shape, and spatial orientation in a field, of an electron with this set of quantum numbers. We speak of electrons *occupying these orbitals*, which is equivalent to saying that the electrons have these special sets of wave characteristics.

4. The Pauli principle restricts the number of electrons that can be accommodated in each orbital. Only two electrons may have the set of quantum numbers (n,l,m_l), and their spins must be paired.

5. The total energy of the atom is found by adding up all the electron-nuclear attractions and subtracting all the electron-electron repulsions. Thus an atom is most stable when its electrons are closest to the nucleus and farthest from one another.

6. The most stable, or ground-state, configuration of an atom will be that with the electrons occupying the most stable (or most strongly binding) set of orbitals permissible within the confines of the Pauli principle.

7. The subshell configurations will be determined by the Hund rule. The most stable configuration will be that with the largest number of unpaired electrons.

8. Screening effects will influence the order of energy for certain subshells. For example the $4s$ orbital is more stable than $3d$ in most neutral atoms.

9. Owing to 8, the unusual stability of a half-filled subshell (e.g., $3d^5$) may result in a rearrangement of the electrons between orbitals (e.g., $4s^1 3d^5$ will be more stable than $4s^2 3d^4$). Similar rearrangements may occur because of the stability of filled shells.

4-4 SOME CHEMICAL USES OF THE PERIODIC TABLE

As a result of the reasoning behind the periodic classification of elements, it will be discovered that many chemical and physical properties of atoms and their compounds are automatically arranged in a rational sequence.

1. Ionization Potentials. From previous discussions we know that, apart from certain irregularities, the ionization potentials increase with increasing atomic number within a given shell. Thus for any row of the periodic table the ionization potentials will increase from left to right. We also know that the binding energy of an electron is greater for the 1*s* orbital than for the 2*s*, which is in turn greater than the 3*s*, and so on. In general, ionization potentials decrease from the top to the bottom of any column in the periodic table.

2. Chemical Similarities. Each vertical column of the table consists of a **group** of elements (congeners), which often have similar chemistry. The first column (group I) contains the **alkali metals** Li to Cs, which are monovalent, chemically reactive metals. Group II is the so-called **alkaline earth elements,** which are divalent metals whose *ns* electrons and vacant *np* orbitals are responsible for most of their chemistry. The next ten columns correspond to the groups of elements with configurations d^0 to d^{10}. These elements are grouped together and called the **transition metals.** Group III is the boron group, in which there is a trend from trivalent metals (In, Tl) to the nonmetallic boron. In this case the principal valence is 3 or 1, by utilization of the *np* or ns^2np orbitals. A similar trend occurs in the carbon group where all the members have some nonmetallic character and the principal valence changes from 4 (C, Si) to 2 (Sn and Pb). In the former case all the outermost electrons participate in the chemistry; for Sn and Pb the inner ns^2 structure is often maintained. Two principal valences (3 and 5) and a trend from metallic to nonmetallic elements characterize the nitrogen group (V), in which the outermost electronic configuration is ns^2np^3. The two-valent oxygen group (VI), and the halogens (group VII) complete the trend toward nonmetals. The chemical similarities that exist among members of a group depends on the fact that atoms in the same columns have similar electron configurations.

3. Atomic Radii. The atomic radius, or covalent radius of an atom is an experimental quantity that refers to one-half the distance between the centers (nuclei) of atoms in a close-packed lattice. The atomic radius increases with increasing atomic number within each group (column). For example the atomic radii of Li, Na, K, Rb, and Cs are 1.33, 1.57, 2.03, 2.16, and 2.35 A, respectively. Notice that the trend in atomic radii is opposite to that of the ionization potentials. This reflects the fact that electrons in orbitals of low binding energy are, on the average, further from the nucleus than those that are tightly bound. Within each **period** (row) the atomic radius decreases with increasing atomic number. The inert gases are the smallest atoms of each period. It follows that Cs and He have, respectively, one of the largest and one of the smallest atomic radii.

Atomic radii are determined to a large extent by the binding energy of the outer electrons of the atom. Since the binding energy of outer electrons is sensitive to screening effects by the inner core, we shall expect screening of the positive charge on the nucleus to be an important factor in descriptions of the sizes of atoms. The Mg atom (1.36 A) is smaller than the Na atom (1.57 A). The two outermost electrons in Mg are in a 3*s* orbital as is the outermost Na electron, but Mg has an extra positive charge on the nucleus, resulting in the two 3*s* electrons of Mg being bound more tightly than the 3*s* electron of Na. For this reason, Ca, Sr, and Ba are smaller than K, Rb, and Cs, respectively. For similar reasons, Al (1.25 A) is smaller than Mg. The influence of nuclear charge is noticeable in the relative atomic radii of the first and second atom in each group of transition metals. Scandium (1.44 A) and yttrium (1.61 A) are larger than titanium (1.32 A) and zirconium (1.45 A), respectively. The decrease in size is again due to the increase by one unit of the nuclear charge.

Throughout each series of transition elements the sizes do not decrease regularly with increasing atomic number as is the case across nontransition rows of the periodic table. There is, however, a regular decrease in size throughout the series of rare earth elements from lanthanum (1.69 A) to hafnium (1.44 A). This relative decrease in size is carried over into other members of the third transition series such as platinum (1.26 A), and gold (1.34 A), which do not show a significant size increase over palladium (1.28 A) and silver (1.34 A) such as might have been expected by direct analogy with the size trends in the alkali and alkaline earth elements. This effect arises because the filled 4*f* subshell of electrons does not provide good screening of the nuclear charge. Consequently the outermost electrons of Au, for example, are subject to a large effective nuclear charge, brought about by the 14 extra protons added to the nucleus during the filling of the $4f$ subshell with electrons.

4. Ionic Radii. Negative ions are larger and positive ions are smaller than their parent atoms. Within any group the ionic radii increase with increasing atomic number. Comparisons within the periods are not so useful because the common ions of elements in different groups usually have different charges. For example, the normal ions of Na, Mg, and Al are Na^+, Mg^{2+} and Al^{3+}, which have ionic radii of 0.98, 0.65, and 0.50 A, respectively. It is true that Mg^+ ($1s^2 2s^2 2p^6 3s^1$) is larger than Na^+ ($1s^2 2s^2 2p^6$), but the comparison is not very useful since Mg does not generally form compounds as a monopositive ion.

Within a group the sizes of negative ions parallel the trend of atomic radii, so one of the largest mononegative ions is I^-, and one of the largest binegative ions is Te^{2-}.

5. Electronic Configurations of Positive Ions. For the first three periods the electronic structures of positive ions are obtained from the atomic configurations by removing the appropriate number of electrons from the outermost occupied orbital. For example, Al^{3+} has the configuration $1s^2 2s^2 2p^6$; this is also the electronic configuration for Na^+, Mg^{2+}, and Si^{4+}, since each ion has the same number of electrons. Such a group of ions is referred to as **isoelectronic.** In turn, each of these ions is isoelectronic with neon.

Certain difficulties arise in the prediction of electronic configurations for transition-metal ions having partially filled d subshells. If the outermost electron in the atom is the first to be ionized, we would expect Ti^{2+} to have the configuration [Ne]$4s^2 3d^0$, obtained by removing the outermost d electrons from Ti ([Ne]$4s^2 3d^2$). However, Ti^{2+} has the configuration [Ne]$3d^2$. The $3d$ and $4s$ orbitals lie at similar energies in the atom with the $4s$ level slightly below the $3d$. The explanation for this is that the $4s$ orbital penetrates the inner electron screen more effectively than the $3d$. The usual energy sequence is reversed for positive ions. The removal of an electron from the atom can be regarded as bringing about an increase of effective nuclear charge. The binding energy of the outer electrons in the ion will be determined to a greater extent by the positions of the peaks of their probability

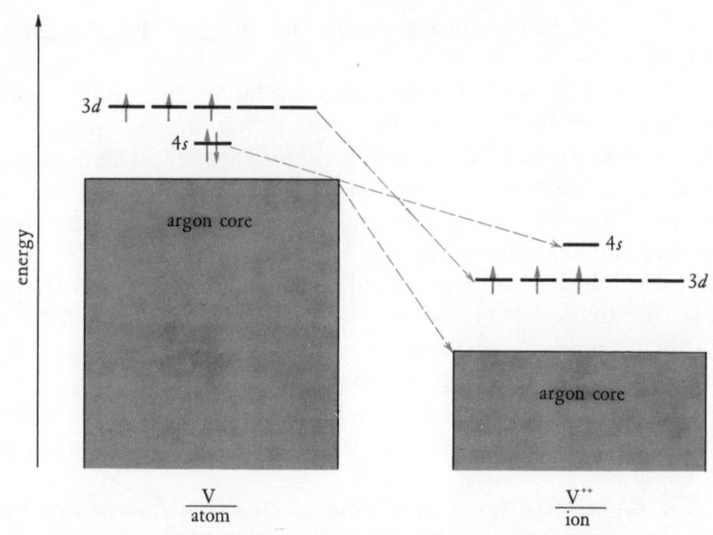

Figure 4–5 The effect of ionization on the order of the 4*s* and 3*d* orbitals of vanadium.

distributions. In the ion the extra penetration of the 4*s* orbital is insufficient to outweigh the 3*d* stabilization caused by the 3*d* electrons being, on the average, closer to the nucleus than 4*s* electrons in the region of the probability maxima. Quite generally, when successive outermost orbitals are close in energy, the order of orbitals in the atom and the ion will not necessarily be identical. Certainly for the divalent transition-metal ions the 4*s* orbital is always less stable than the 3*d* orbitals (see Fig. 4–5).[1]

PROBLEMS

1. Write out the electron configurations for the following: Mg, Cl, V, Cr^{3+}, Ni^{2+}, Ge, Cs, Zn^{2+}

---

[1] According to electrostatics a spherically symmetric charge distribution can be replaced by a point charge at its center. Hence nuclear charge that is experienced by any one electron is influenced by the presence of other electrons: This is an alternative way of regarding screening effects.

2. Why is the ionization potential of oxygen higher than that of nitrogen?

3. Give two examples of each of the following:

(*a*) an atom with a completed outer shell

(*b*) an atom with a half-filled subshell

(*c*) an atom with its outer electrons occupying a half-filled, and a filled subshell

(*d*) an atom with completely filled subshells but with an incomplete shell

4. Arrange the following sets of atoms in order of increasing atomic radius:

(*a*) Na, Rb, K, Mg
(*b*) Na, Si, Al, Ar
(*c*) Ne, Kr, Ar, C, F
(*d*) Ca, Zn, Cd, Hg, Sr

5. Arrange the following sets of atoms in order of increasing ionization potential:

(*a*) Na, P, Si, Al, S
(*b*) K, Cs, Rb, Ca
(*c*) As, Br, Se
(*d*) V, Mn, Cr, Fe

6. How many unpaired electrons are present in each of the following? N, O, P, Ba, V, Mo, Re, Fe^{2+}, Cu, Cu^{2+}, Cu^{1+}

7. By applying the reasoning in the last two paragraphs of Sec. 4–2, explain why K and Sc^{2+} do not have the same electronic configuration.

8. From the Balmer spectral data of Chap. I, compute the ionization potential for an electron in a 2*s* orbital of hydrogen. Why is this value different from the first ionization potential of lithium?

V

Energy Terms and States of Atoms

THIS CHAPTER DEALS WITH the systematic naming of the electronic states of atoms. To do this effectively the student will have to learn and understand the rules that are set out at the beginning of each section. The last three sections deal, respectively, with hydrogen-like, alkali-like, and many-electron spectra. These sections are not self-contained and a grasp of earlier notions is necessary to understand what follows. The remaining chapters of the book will assume a knowledge of the spectroscopic-state designations described below.

5–1 A MORE FORMAL DESCRIPTION OF THE ENERGY OF AN ATOM

The structural details of atomic spectra are accounted for theoretically by solving the equations of motion of the electrons in the atom. The theory must contain a formal account of all possible contributions to the energy of the atom.

1. Atomic Configurations. The *total kinetic energy* of the electrons and the *electrons-to-nucleus attractive energy* of the atom are the factors that determine the energy of a configuration. The energy of the atom arising from these sources can be completely defined by the quantum numbers n and l. Atomic configurations therefore relate only to the orbital motion of electrons.

2. ***Atomic Terms.*** Terms are defined for a particular set of quantum numbers n, l, and s for each electron in the atom.

3. ***Atomic Energy Levels.*** Levels are defined by n, l, and s and include a description of the coupling mechanism of the orbital and spin motions of the electrons. Each level refers to a particular value of the *total angular momentum* of the atom, which is generally comprised of combinations of the spin and orbital angular momenta.

4. ***The Multiplicity of a Term.*** The number of levels that correspond to the same term is the multiplicity of the term.

5. ***Atomic States.*** The effect of a magnetic field on an atom is to split each level into a number of states. The number of states into which a given level can be split in a magnetic field is the **multiplicity of the level.** The effect of a magnetic field on spectral lines will be discussed in Chap. VIII. Let it suffice to mention for now that all four quantum numbers, n, l, m_l, and s, serve to define a state.

Very often when the effect of magnetic fields is not being considered, levels as described above are referred to as states. For example during the previous chapters we have employed the word "state" quite often when according to the above definitions we should have used "level." In this chapter the five definitions above will be rigidly adhered to. The student will soon realize that, when a symbol is associated with a designation such as a term, the symbol itself will be enough to indicate that a term is under consideration.

6. ***Individual and Total Angular Momenta.*** Conventionally the orbital and spin angular momentum quantum numbers for individual electrons are written as the lowercase letters l and s, respectively. For example, if there are two electrons in the atom, their orbital angular momentum quantum numbers are written l_1 and l_2; the spin quantum numbers are s_1 and s_2. The total orbital quantum number is a composite of the l values for each electron and is written L, the total orbital quantum number. We shall dis-

cover below that L can take values of 0, 1, 2, . . . , etc., depending on the value of l for each electron. By analogy with the s, p, d, and f symbols, which are used to describe the value of l, we use the symbols S, P, D, and F to describe values of $L = 0, 1, 2$, or 3. Similarly capital S describes the total spin quantum number, which is a composite of the s values for each electron.

The total angular momentum quantum number for each electron is derived from the l and s values for that electron and is designated by j. The total angular momentum quantum number for the atom, which is derived from L and S for all electrons, is written as J.

Using these symbols, we are now in a position to give more precise definitions corresponding to definitions 2, 3, and 4 above.

2′. An atomic term is usually written

$$^{2S+1}L$$

For example, if $S = 1$ and $L = 2$, the term is ^3D.

3′. An atomic level is designated by

$$^{2S+1}L_J$$

For example, when $S = 1$, $L = 2$, and $J = 2$, the level is $^3D_2$.

4′. The expression $(2S + 1)$ is not the multiplicity of the term unless $L > S$. We can call $(2S + 1)$ the spin multiplicity when $L > S$ but it has no significance other than its relation to the number of unpaired electrons in the atom.

The next step is to discover how the total angular momentum quantum numbers are derived from the individual quantum numbers. To this end we shall discuss particular atoms in order of increasing complexity.

5–2 HYDROGEN-LIKE ATOMS

Since the configurations for hydrogen atoms are much simpler than for many-electron atoms, we shall first discuss the one-electron case. Electronic transitions involve the promotion or demotion of the electron from one orbital to another. Each configuration is characterized by (n,l) for the electron. Thus the configuration (1,0) [i.e., $1s^1$] corresponds to the ^2S term ($L = l = 0$, $S = s = \frac{1}{2}$). The **spin multiplicity** of the state is equal to $2S + 1$ where S is the total (one-electron) spin angular momentum quantum number in this case equal to $\frac{1}{2}$. The orbital angular momentum for the ^2S term is zero ($l = 0$), and the only possible value for the angular momentum quantum number of the atom (J) in this term is $\frac{1}{2}$. The resulting level is $^2S_{1/2}$. The spin and orbital angular momenta have *direction*, so they can only be added in certain ways: They must be added in such manner that *the various J values differ from one another by integral numbers;* also *J must be positive.* The possible values of J are

$$J = (L + S), \qquad (L + S - 1), \qquad (L + S - 2), \ldots |L - S|$$

Let us consider the proper designation of the term corresponding to the configuration $2p^1$ of the H atom. In this case $L = l = 1$, $S = s = \frac{1}{2}$. Thus the term is 2^2P (read as two–doublet–P). The possible values of J are

$$J = (1 + \tfrac{1}{2}), \qquad (1 + \tfrac{1}{2} - 1) = \tfrac{3}{2}, \qquad \tfrac{1}{2}$$

Thus our ^2P term in reality corresponds to two levels differing in their total angular momentum. The value of J is usually written as a subscript to the term symbol. Thus the two levels arising from the configuration $2p^1$ are $2^2P_{1/2}$ and $2^2P_{3/2}$. Notice that no other values of J are possible, since the next term in the sequence, $(1 + \frac{1}{2} - 2)$, is negative.

The two J levels would have the same energy if it were assumed that the orbital and spin motions of the electron did not influence each other. The coupling between orbital and spin angular momenta is extremely slight for hydrogen, amounting to fractions of a wave number, which is a very small portion of the energy of the term. For example the $1^2S - 2^2P$ term separation is 83,000 cm^{-1}, but the $^2P_{1/2} - {}^2P_{3/2}$ level separation is less than 0.1 cm^{-1}.

Let us examine the various levels for a d^1 configuration of hydrogen. In this case $L = l = 2$, $S = s = \frac{1}{2}$.

$$J = (2 + \tfrac{1}{2}), \qquad (2 + \tfrac{1}{2}) - 1$$

Therefore

$$J = \tfrac{5}{2}, \qquad \tfrac{3}{2}$$

Thus the d^1 configuration gives rise to two levels $^2D_{5/2}$ and $^2D_{3/2}$, which will be close in energy. Notice that $J = \frac{1}{2}$ is not a permitted value of the total angular-momentum quantum number, since the smallest possible value of J is $L - S = 2 - \frac{1}{2} = \frac{3}{2}$. Similarly the two ^2F states arising from the configuration f^1 are $^2F_{7/2}$ and $^2F_{5/2}$. Note that every term ^2L of hydrogen, except ^2S, is in reality two levels, which will be at slightly different energies. The number of levels is $2S + 1$ except in the case where $l = 0$ (see *4'* above). A portion of the emission spectrum of H atoms is diagrammatically represented in Fig. 5–1. The transition depicted is the $3^2D \rightarrow 2^2P$ orbital demotion. In normal spectrographs the Balmer series appears as a series of sharp lines whose energies can be fitted to the Ritz formula. One of these lines occurs at 6562.8 A and is called H_α, since it is the first line of the Balmer series. The H_α line corresponds to a $3^2D \rightarrow 2^2P$ emission. When the line is scrutinized under very high resolution it is seen to be composed of a few narrower lines. The line has **fine structure.** Some of the fine structure and its origin is shown in Fig. 5–1. With spin-orbital interaction each of the terms ^2P and ^2D are split into doublets. The transitions that are indicated by vertical lines can then occur, and the resulting spectrum has the fine structure shown at the lower part of the diagram. Notice that *all the possible transitions do not occur;* for example, the line corresponding to $^2D_{5/2} \rightarrow {}^2P_{1/2}$ is absent from the spectrum (dashed line). Experimental considerations of this sort and results from quantum mechanics lead to the formulation of **selection rules,** which enable us to predict which of the various possible electronic transitions will occur and to what extent they occur. The selection rules for transitions between levels is that these can only occur when J changes by $+1$, -1, or 0. This selection rule is usually written

$$\Delta J = \pm 1 \qquad \text{or} \qquad 0$$

where ΔJ (read as delta–J) means the change in J. This rule implies that the transitions $^2D_{5/2} \rightarrow {}^2P_{3/2}$ ($\Delta J = 1$), $^2D_{3/2} \rightarrow {}^2P_{3/2}$ ($\Delta J = 0$), and $^2D_{3/2} \rightarrow {}^2P_{1/2}$ ($\Delta J = 1$) are *allowed,* whereas the transition $^2D_{5/2} \rightarrow {}^2P_{1/2}$ ($\Delta J = 2$) is *forbidden.* A spectral line that in reality consists of a few closely spaced or fine-structure components is called a **multiplet.** Hydrogen-like spectral lines are

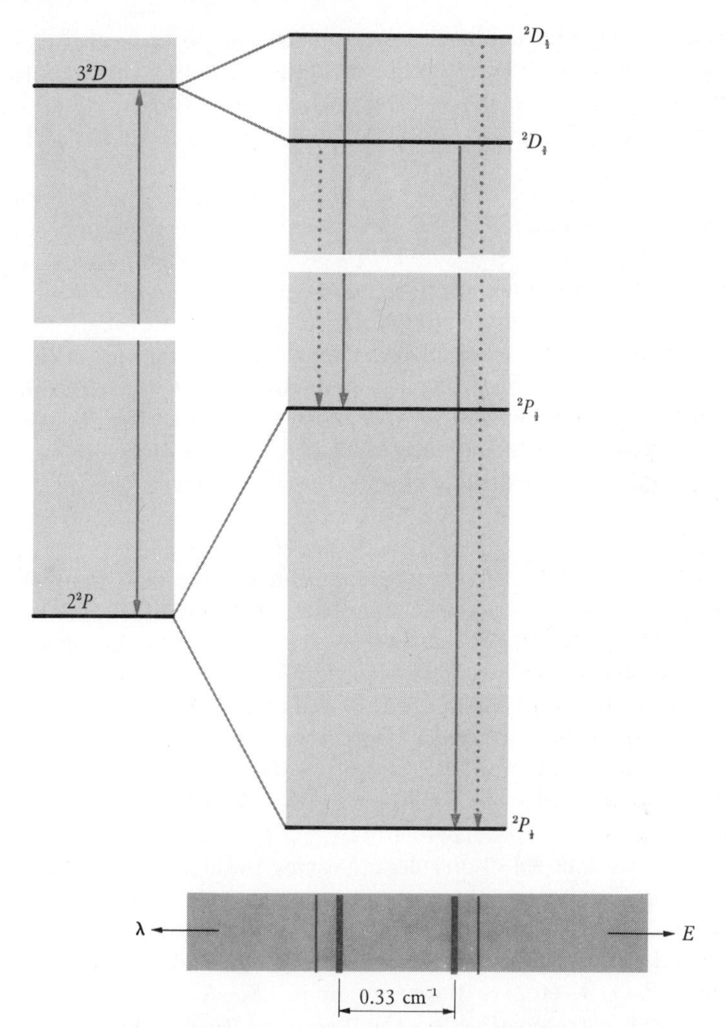

Figure 5–1 The fine structure of the hydrogen $3^{2}D \rightarrow 2^{2}P$ transition; the spin-orbital and $^{2}P-^{2}D$ splittings are on very different scales. The center of the multiplet is at cm^{-1}.

always compound doublets. As a final example of levels in hydrogen, let us scrutinize the fine structure of a $4^2F \rightarrow 3^2D$ transition. The J values for the ^2F term are

$$J = (3 + \tfrac{1}{2}), \qquad (3 + \tfrac{1}{2} - 1)$$
$$J = \tfrac{7}{2}, \qquad \tfrac{5}{2}$$

thus the transition $^2F \rightarrow {}^2D$ will consist of three components $^2F_{7/2} \rightarrow {}^2F_{5/2}$, $^2F_{5/2} \rightarrow {}^2D_{5/2}$, and $^2F_{5/2} \rightarrow {}^2D_{3/2}$. In the actual spectrum two of these lines are strong and one is weak and the $^2F \rightarrow {}^2D$ line appears as a compound doublet.

So far we have not placed any restriction on the possible changes of total orbital angular momentum during an electronic transition. The selection rule for L can be deduced theoretically, and a detailed investigation of multiplets in atomic spectra have completely confirmed the theoretical predictions; viz.,

$$\Delta L = \pm 1$$

The orbital angular momentum quantum number can change by one unit during the electronic transition. It follows that the transitions $^2S \rightarrow {}^2P$, $^2P \rightarrow {}^2D$, $^2D \rightarrow {}^2F$, and so on are allowed, whereas $^2S \rightarrow {}^2D$ and $^2P \rightarrow {}^2F$ are forbidden. So each of the transitions discussed earlier in this chapter are allowed on two counts—on orbital and on spin-orbital grounds. Both these selection rules must be adhered to; for example, the transition $^2D_{3/2} \rightarrow {}^2S_{1/2}$ is allowed by the J selection rules but forbidden by the rule $\Delta L = \pm 1$, and the transition is formally forbidden.

There are no selection rules governing the changes in principal quantum number, so this may change by 0, 1, 2, 3, etc. The Lyman series of hydrogen, which is observed in absorption, corresponds to the series of transitions $1^2S_{1/2} \rightarrow n^2P$, where n has the values 2, 3, 4, etc., to the series limit. Each line is in reality a doublet corresponding to the two transitions $1^2S_{1/2} \rightarrow n^2P_{1/2}$ ($\Delta J = 0$) and $1^2S_{1/2} \rightarrow n^2P_{3/2}$ ($\Delta J = 1$), which are very nearly at the same energy.

All those species that have ground configurations like hydrogen have hydrogen-like doublet spectra. For example He^+ and Li^{2+} each have the ground configuration $1s^1$ and their spectra resemble that of hydrogen atoms. Of course the actual energies of the levels are not identical to those for hydrogen, but the type of series and multiplets are similar. We shall now summarize the principal features of hydrogen-like spectra:

1. The total angular momentum J can have two values corresponding to each L; i.e., $J = L + S$; there is only one value for $L = 0$, namely $J = \frac{1}{2}$.

2. Terms with the same n are at the same energy, that is, the $2S$ and $2P$ terms have the same energy; so do the $3S$, $3P$, and $3D$ terms.

3. Spin-orbit coupling provides for a very small difference in energy between levels of different J but with the same value of n and L (see p. 95).

4. The selection rules for electronic transitions are

$$\Delta n = 0,\ 1,\ 2,\ \text{etc.},$$
$$\Delta L = \pm 1$$
$$\Delta J = 0,\ \pm 1$$

5. Transitions for which the criteria of paragraph 4 are not upheld are forbidden and may not appear in the normal spectrum. The other transitions are allowed and appear in the spectrum.

6. The spin of the electron endows each term with its doublet character, and transitions between these doublets cause the appearance of multiplet fine structure of spectral lines.

5–3 THE SPECTRA OF ALKALI METALS

The electronic configurations of the alkali metals are [inert gas]ns^1; for example, Li, Na, and K have the configuration [He]$2s^1$, [Ne]$3s^1$, and [Ar]$4s^1$, respectively. According to our discussions of electronic structure, the inner electrons in the filled shells are drawn very close to the nucleus and much of the "size" of these atoms arises from the distant location of the outer s electron. It has proved reasonable to assume that the inner core of electrons is relatively inert and that the optical properties of alkali metals will be due to the outer electron. However *we would not expect hydrogen-like spectra* because the condition 2 above, will be violated. The unoccupied s, p, d, and f orbitals of the alkali-metal atoms are each screened from the nucleus by the inner core of electrons, but *each is screened to a different extent.* Thus orbitals with different l and the same n are not at the same energy. The difference between hydrogen-like and alkali spectra is caused by the relative spacings of levels in each shell. The subshells for $n = 3$ are shown in Fig. 5–2. In the alkali atom the sets of $3s$, $3p$, and $3d$ orbitals are not at the same energy, although the individual orbitals for a given l (i.e., the five $3d$ orbitals) are still at the same energy. The selection rules from the previous section are applicable but no simple series relationships can be found in the alkali spectra. This is because the separation between s, p, and d orbitals depends on the value of n, becoming less as n increases. However we still see series limits from which ionization potentials can be obtained. The

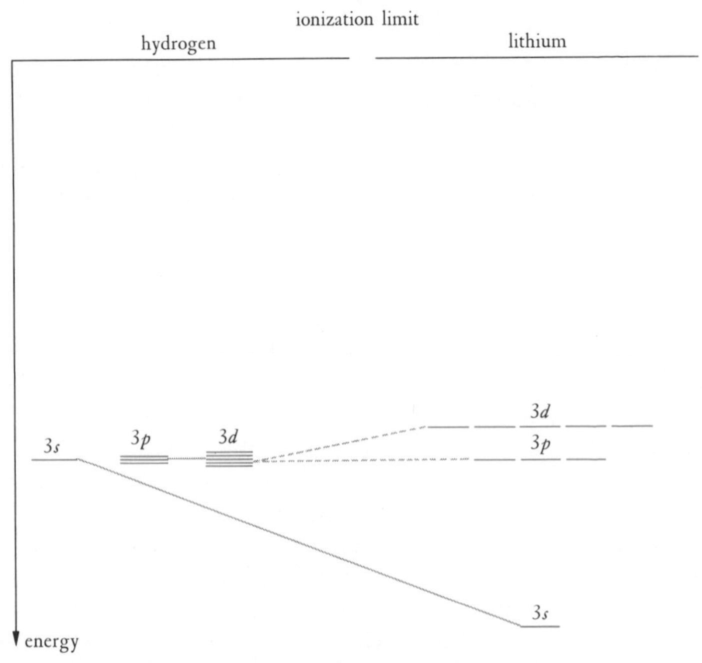

Figure 5–2 The relative energies of orbitals with $n = 3$ for hydrogen and lithium.

absorption spectrum of sodium vapor is shown in Plate I. This series of lines is analogous to the Lyman series of hydrogen and involves transitions between the ground configuration $[\mathrm{Ne}]3s^1$ and the excited configurations $[\mathrm{Ne}]3s^0np^1$, where $n = 4, 5, \ldots$, etc. Each line in this spectrum has complex doublet fine structure. The core electrons do not contribute to the total angular momentum, since their resultant spin is zero (Pauli principle) and their total orbital angular momentum is also zero (filled shells). Figure 5–3 shows the arrangement of a few of the levels of K and

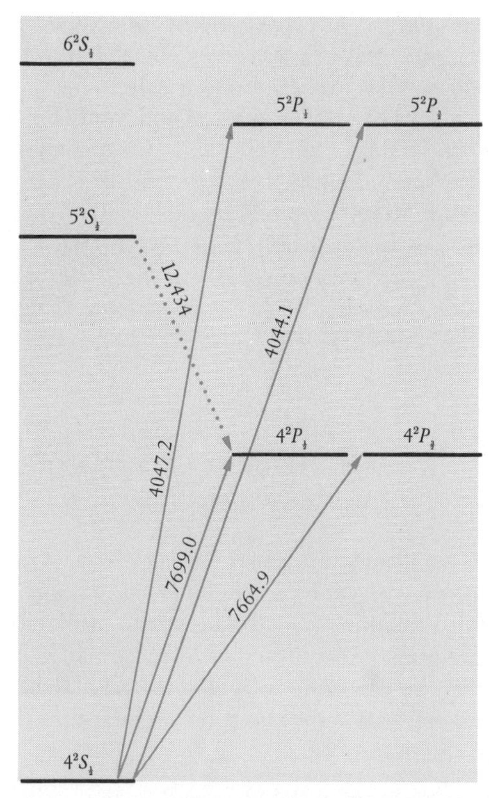

Figure 5–3 The low-lying levels of the potassium atom, showing the origin of the doublet fine structure. The numbers are wavelengths in Å.

illustrates the origin of the doublets. The emission lines $5^2S_{1/2} \rightarrow 4^2P$ are also represented on the diagram. With this added information it is possible to estimate the relative *ns-np* energy separations for principal quantum numbers 4 and 5 (see Problem 6). Notice that the spin-orbit splitting decreases with increasing principal quantum number, and, as before, the level with highest J is the highest-energy component of each doublet. The magnitude of the doublet splitting increases with increasing atomic number. Thus the splitting for Li ($2^2P_{1/2} \rightarrow 2^2P_{3/2}$) is 0.337 cm^{-1}, whereas for K the splitting is 57.7 cm^{-1} ($4^2P_{1/2} \rightarrow 4^2P_{3/2}$).

As an example of the fine structure of alkali-metal spectral lines, we shall examine the well-known sodium D-line, which is the emission that causes the bright yellow color from sodium lamps. The transitions involved are from the excited levels $3^2P_{1/2}$, $3^2P_{3/2}$ to the ground level $3^2S_{1/2}$. The ground and excited configurations are, respectively, [Ne]$3s^1$ and [Ne]$3s^03p^1$. Both components of the upper doublet can combine with the ground levels ($L = 1$, $J = 0$ or 1), so the sodium D-line is in reality a doublet. The two spectral lines have energies 16,960.9 cm^{-1} and 16,978.1 cm^{-1}. The spin-orbital coupling energy, which separates the ^2P terms, is just the difference between the energies of the two lines in the doublet, that is, 17.2 cm^{-1}.

5-4 THE SPECTRA OF ALKALINE EARTHS AND Zn, Cd, AND Hg

Each of these elements has an inert core with an outer ns^2 configuration. In Zn, Cd, and Hg the inner $3d$, $4d$, and $5d$ (and $4f$) orbitals are filled but the optically important electrons are the ns^2 pair. When two electrons are considered we shall see a further development of the use of L and S for the total orbital and spin quantum numbers, and J for the total angular-momentum quantum number. So, as before,

$$J = (L + S), (L + S - 1), (L + S - 2) \ . \ . \ . \ |L - S|$$

and L and S are given by analogous rules:

$$L = (l_1 + l_2), \qquad (l_1 + l_2 - 1), \qquad (l_1 + l_2 - 2) \ldots |l_1 - l_2|$$
$$S = |\tfrac{1}{2} + \tfrac{1}{2}|, \ |\tfrac{1}{2} - \tfrac{1}{2}|$$

In this case the different values of L and S can give rise to more possibilities than we have previously found. We use the same symbols to describe the terms and levels. A term for which $L = 1$ is called a P term, but now *this does not necessarily imply a configuration in which an electron is in a p orbital.*

The ground-state designation is obtained as follows: The lowest energy configuration is ns^2; thus the total spin S is simply $(\frac{1}{2} - \frac{1}{2}) = 0$. The multiplicity of the term is therefore $2S + 1 = 1$, i.e., a *singlet* term. The orbital quantum number is zero for each electron thus $L = (l_1 + l_2) = 0$, so the term is of ^1S type. The possible values of J are simply $(L + S) = (0 + 0) = 0$, so the lowest-energy configuration gives rise to just one level–$^1S_0$.[1]

The next most stable configuration is ns^1np^1. In this case $l_1 = 0$ and $l_2 = 1$, so $L = (0 + 1), (0 + 1) - 1$; that is, there are two terms arising from this configuration—one of $P(L = 1)$ and another of $S(L = 0)$ type. The total spin can be either 1 or 0, depending on whether the two electrons have the same or opposed spins. The value $S = 1$ gives rise to triplet terms $[(2 \times 1) + 1 = 3]$, and $S = 0$ gives rise to singlet terms. First we shall consider the triplets, since we know from previous considerations (see the discussion of electron repulsion and the Hund rule in Sec. 4–1) that these will be the most stable excited levels. For the ^3S term the possible values of J are

$$J = 0 + 1 = 1$$

and there is one ^3S level—$^3S_1$. For the triplet P term (^3P) the possible values of J are

$$J = (1 + 1), \qquad (1 + 1 - 1), \qquad (1 + 1 - 2)$$
$$J = 2, 1, 0$$

There are three levels of the type ^3P; these are $^3P_2$, $^3P_1$, and $^3P_0$. As before these levels are very close in energy unless the atomic

[1] The spins can be added in this simple manner because of the definition of S as a projection along a fixed reference axis.

number is large (see p. 95). For the singlet multiplicity the possible levels are $^1S_0$, $^1P_0$, and $^1P_1$. The student should verify this using the above method.

Finally we shall work out the levels that arise from the configuration ns^1nd^1. The multiplicity is either singlet or triplet as before; $l_1 = 0$, $l_2 = 2$; thus the J values are

$$\begin{aligned} J(\text{singlet}) &= (2 + 0) = 2 \\ J(\text{triplet}) &= (2 + 1), \qquad (2 + 1 - 1), \qquad (2 + 1 - 1) \\ &= 3,\ 2,\ 1 \end{aligned}$$

The levels from this configuration are therefore (for the moment neglecting the principal quantum number) $^1D_2$, $^3D_3$, $^3D_2$, and $^3D_1$.

The student should notice that the levels with J (singlet) $=$ $(2 + 0 - 1)$ cannot occur because the smallest possible value of J is $|L - S|$. This obtains because of the space quantization, or the quantum restrictions on the direction of the total angular momentum. These directional properties are illustrated in Fig. 5–4, where the case of J (triplet) is examined. The value of L is 2, represented by an arrow of length two units directed upward. The spin momentum quantum number is 1, along this axis. The L and

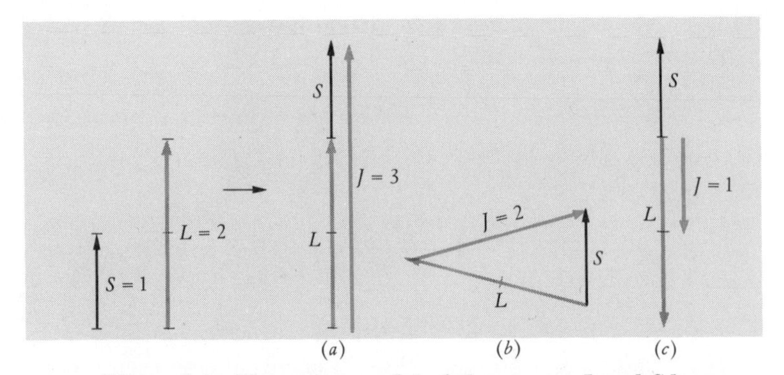

Figure 5–4 The vector model of the atom. L and S have directional properties and their resultants (J values) are space-quantized. Thus only three values of J are permitted when $S = 1$, $L = 2$.

S must be combined such that the resultant combinations (J values) differ from one another by integral numbers. One combination is L and S in the same direction (Fig. 5–4a), which gives a resultant of 3 units ($J = 3$). A value of $J = 2$ can be obtained if an arrow representing the orbital quantum number is directed such that it forms the base of an isosceles triangle where the side of length L equals the side of length J. The value $J = 1$ is obtained by opposing the directions of L and S. No other orientation of L and S can give rise to a J value that is a whole number and the value of 0 can never be obtained with these values of L and S.

Until now we have discussed only the quantum numbers for angular momentum and not the actual magnitude of the momentum. The total orbital angular momentum is $L^*(h/2\pi)$ where $L^* = \sqrt{L(L+1)}$ and L takes the values given above. Similarly the spin angular momentum is $S^*(h/2\pi)$ where $S^* = \sqrt{S(S+1)}$ and the total angular momentum is $J^*(h/2\pi)$ where $J^* = \sqrt{J(J+1)}$. These results come from quantum mechanics and cannot be proved here. The student should note that in the geometric method outlined above (often called the vector method) for evaluating the possible values of J, the length of each line should have been made equal to the angular momentum. This is because it is the angular momentum that is space-quantized. However the above technique yields the proper values of the quantum number J.

From the above discussion it will be clear that the spectra of alkaline earth atoms and of Zn, Cd, and Hg will consist of series of single lines due to transitions between singlet levels, and series of triplet lines (i.e., lines which have triplet fine structure) due to transitions between the triplet levels and from singlet to triplet levels.

Finally, one further selection rule must be introduced. *Transitions between levels of different multiplicity are forbidden.* If this selection rule were rigorous, singlet-triplet transitions would never be observed, but in fact they are usually detectable. However, the probability is considerably greater for transitions involving no change in multiplicity. In the next chapter we shall examine some experimental factors that will enable us to estimate the "allowedness" or forbiddenness of a given transition.

5–5 A MORE PHYSICAL DESCRIPTION OF ATOMIC STATES

At the beginning of this chapter a few rules to be memorized were described. It is the purpose of this section to provide certain physical justifications for these rules.

Electron Repulsion

The energy derived from this source causes the splitting between terms. If the energy of interaction between electrons in a given configuration were excluded from the calculations we would find that all terms arising from a single configuration would have the same energy. The interelectron interactions can therefore be regarded as causing each configuration to split into terms having different L and S quantum numbers and of course different energies. Normally the terms with the highest multiplicity are at lowest energy according to the Hund rule. For a given multiplicity the terms with the highest value of L will lie at lowest energy. To illustrate this, we shall discuss the splitting into terms of the lowest-energy configuration of the carbon atom, $1s^2 2s^2 2p^2$. The S electrons may be considered as occupying very stable orbitals, and so the principal optical properties of carbon derive from the two $2p$ electrons. Because the electrons are each in a p subshell we have $l_1 = l_2 = 1$. Thus the possible values of L are 2, 1, and 0 corresponding to D, P, and S terms. The origin of these terms is shown in Fig. 5–5, using the vector model. The vectors represent the magnitude (1 unit) and spatial orientation of electron angular momenta. The three terms that result are the only three for which L is an integer. They correspond to different energies, since the mode of interaction (i.e., electron-electron interaction) is different for each case. The least repulsion arises when both electrons have the same angular momentum vectors (i.e., when $L = 2$). The electrostatic repulsions are greatest when the angular momenta are equal and opposite.

The possible values of S are 0 and 1 (singlet or triplet). However for the configuration np^2 we cannot simply conclude that there are six terms, three triplets, and three singlets. In the previ-

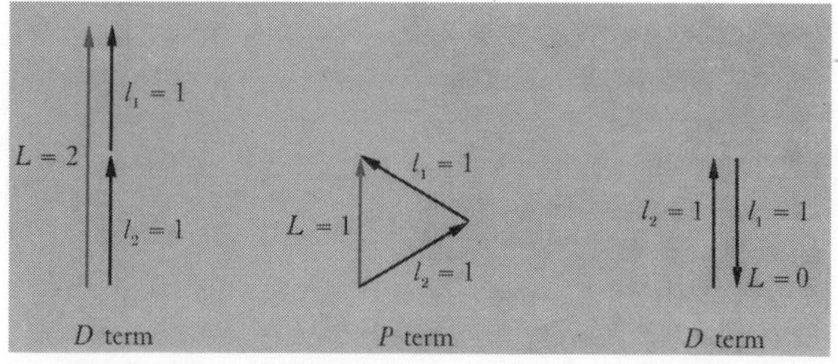

Figure 5–5 The addition of angular momenta (l) to provide the possible values of total angular momentum in a two-electron atom.

ous examples the electrons were not in *equivalent orbitals.* The p subshell consists of three equivalent orbitals, so we must ascertain whether all the above terms are possible within the confines of the Pauli exclusion principle. The only restriction is that each electron must have a different set of four quantum numbers (n,l,m_l,s). The electrons have n and l in common so the difference must lie with m_l and s. Remembering that m_l can take the values of $\pm l$, $\pm(l-1)$, . . . , 0, we conclude that both m_{l1} and m_{l2} (m_l quantum numbers for electrons 1 and 2, respectively) can take the values of 1, 0, and -1. The values of m_l associated with the total angular momentum will be called m_L. The possible values of m_L are obtained from $\pm L$, $\pm(L-1)$, . . . , 0 in the same way as for the individual m_l values. Thus the values of m_L are:

$$\begin{array}{ccccc l} 2 & 1 & 0 & -1 & 2 & \text{from } L = 2 \quad (D) \\ & 1 & 0 & -1 & & \text{from } L = 1 \quad (P) \\ & & 0 & & & \text{from } L = 0 \quad (S) \end{array}$$

The above nine values of m_L could have been obtained directly by taking all possible combinations of $(m_{l_1} + m_{l_2})$. Suppose now that $S = 1$. We are then considering the triplet term, for which the two electrons must have the same spin quantum number. In order to satisfy the Pauli principle, the electrons must necessarily have different values of m_l. Consider the values of m_L that can arise when $m_l \neq m_{l2}$. If $m_{l1} = 1$, then m_L (for $m_{l1} \neq m_{l2}$) can have values of 1 and 0; if $m_{l1} = 0$, then $m_L = 1$

or -1; if $m_{l_1} = -1$, it follows that $m_L = 0$ or -1. In other words, the only possible set of values of m_L, for $m_{l_1} \neq m_{l_2}$, are -1, 0, and 1. It follows that the term for $L = 1$ is a triplet. So far we have found a ^3P term, and in so doing have used up three of the nine values of m_L. Notice that a ^3D term would be excluded by the Pauli principle, since this term contains a value of $m_L = 2$ that could only be derived from the sum of $m_{l_1} = 1$ and $m_{l_2} = 1$. If this were the case, the two electrons would have the same set of quantum numbers $(n,1,1,\frac{1}{2})$. The remaining terms are singlets, namely, ^1S and ^1D. The argument is less involved for singlets because the electrons can have the same values of m.

The primary splitting of the np^2 configuration by electronic interactions is shown in Fig. 5–6. The ^3P term is at lowest energy (Hund's rule), and the ^1D term is at lower energy than ^1S.

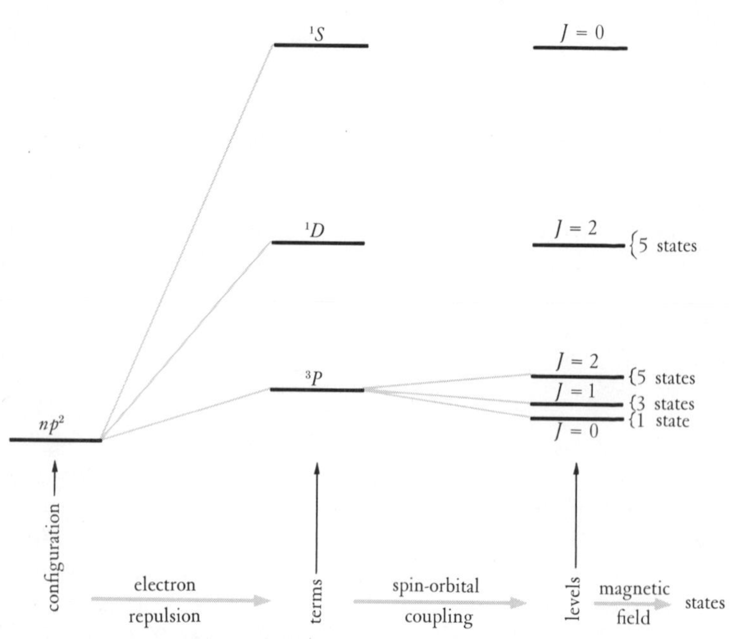

Figure 5–6 The splitting of the np^2 configuration into terms, levels, and states.

Spin-orbit Coupling

In many-electron atoms the electrostatic energies described above can be fairly large—on the order of an electron volt. The splitting of terms into levels, on the other hand, is much smaller than this for light atoms. Thus for light atoms the electronic interactions are usually treated before spin-orbit coupling. The terms are split because each electron has a **magnetic moment** of momentum (or spin angular momentum) which can interact with, and influence, its orbital motion. The earlier statement that this effect is small in comparison with electrostatic interactions implies that our previous restrictions on orbital motion are not severely influenced by spin-orbit coupling. It is consequently justifiable to form our skeleton of atomic structure by first coupling L and S vectors as above. This approach to atomic energy levels is called LS coupling or Russell-Saunders coupling. For heavy atoms the spin-orbit coupling can be very large—implying that the orbital motion of electrons is considerably modified by the spin motion. In the latter event our skeleton of levels is built up by first coupling the individual l and s values to give a j for the angular momentum of each electron, and subsequently combining the individual j's to give the total angular momentum. This type of coupling is named jj coupling. We shall only consider LS coupling.[1]

Spin-orbital coupling in atoms arises because of magnetic interactions between the two magnetic fields associated with electronic motion. Orbital and spin motions of the electron each give rise to a magnetic field (see Chap. VIII for further details). The two fields influence one another, thus providing a means for the interaction of the two motions. The extent of the interaction depends on the magnitude of the spin and orbital angular momenta. Thus the various levels (corresponding to the possible values of J) are at different energies in the atom. We therefore regard the terms as being split into levels under spin-orbit interactions. The interaction splits each term into either $(2S + 1)$ or $(2L + 1)$ energy levels, which are distinguished by their values of J. We

[1] An everyday example of classical spin-orbit coupling is the precession of the earth in its orbit around the sun. This is caused by mechanical coupling of the rotational and orbital angular momenta of the earth in the gravitational field of the sun.

shall see in Chap. VIII that in a magnetic field these levels can be further split into $(2J + 1)$ states characterized by their values of m_L.

The magnitude of the spin-orbit-interaction energy is highly dependent on the nuclear charge of the atom. The magnetic moment arising from the orbital motion of the electron may be represented by a magnetic dipole at the center of the orbit, i.e., at the nucleus. The magnetic moment that is due to spin can be described by a dipole at the site of the spinning electron. In less classical terms the location of the spin dipole will be described by a probability distribution, and the orbital magnetic dipole will remain at the center of the charge distribution. Spin-orbital interaction is caused by the interactions between these magnetic dipoles. Classical theory tells us that dipole-dipole interaction falls off as $1/r^3$, where r is the separation of the dipoles. Terms in $1/r^3$ are relatively large only when r is very small. It follows that the main contribution to spin-orbit coupling will arise when the electron is very close to the nucleus. This effect produces a strong dependence of spin-orbit interactions on the nuclear charge (see, for example, Fig. 6–2).

Spin-orbit coupling is effective in breaking down the selection rules that prohibit electronic transitions between terms of different multiplicity. The magnetic coupling of the spin and orbital motions of the electrons in the atom tends to mix up the multiplicities of the terms. For example, singlet terms $(S = 0)$ take on the character of higher multiplicities, e.g., triplet, because the orbital part of the singlet term interacts with the spin part of other terms. It follows that the spin-only or orbital-only selection rule will no longer be rigorous. As a result L and S are not "good quantum numbers," and this is especially true when the spin-orbit interaction is large as is found for heavy atoms.

5–6 SUMMARY

1. The principal features of hydrogen-like spectra are summarized earlier in the chapter. Spectra of this type are exhibited by one-electron species with no inner electron core, such as H, He^+,

and Li^{2+}. The spectral lines can be arranged into simple series because there are no electron-electron interactions. States with orbital angular momentum quantum numbers 0, 1, 2, 3, etc., are labeled S, P, D, F, etc. The spin quantum number S is always $\frac{1}{2}$ so the spin multiplicity of every state is 2. Each term (e.g., ^2P) is a doublet, there being two possible values of the total angular momentum quantum number for each term. The only exception to this is the ^2S term for which there is only one value of J. The total angular momentum of the atom in a level of given J is $(h/2\pi)\sqrt{J(J+1)}$.

2. The alkali metals do not have simple series spectra because the electron-electron interactions (screening) depend on the orbital angular momentum. The spectra can be considered as resulting from the one electron, the ns electron, being promoted to p, d, and f orbitals of higher principal quantum number. Since the ground term ^2S has only one j value ($j = \frac{1}{2}$), the spectral lines corresponding to s-p promotions are each doublets. The doublet splitting increases with increasing atomic number of the alkali metal and decreases with increasing principal quantum number within a given spectral series.

3. Many-electron spectra: The number and types of states that arise from a given configuration depend on the total angular momentum quantum numbers L and S. The composite angular momentum quantum number J can take the values

$$J = (L + S), \qquad (L + S - 1), \ . \ . \ . \ |L - S|$$

The total angular momentum of the system in any level is $(h/2\pi)\sqrt{J(J+1)}$. As before, the levels for a given L and S are at the same energy unless there is spin-orbital interaction. In this event each will split into $(2S + 1)$ levels if S is less than L; otherwise the state will split into $(2L + 1)$ levels. The restrictions on J, shown above, are due to the fact that L and S cannot combine in an arbitrary fashion. The total angular momentum $(h/2\pi)\sqrt{J(J+1)}$ must be quantized in space.

4. Transitions involving a change in multiplicity are forbidden. We shall see in the next chapter that the expressions "allowed" and "forbidden" are only rigorous to certain degrees of approximation.

PROBLEMS

1. Indicate the spectroscopic terms and levels associated with each of the following electron configurations (consider only the outermost orbitals):

(*a*) $1s^22s^1$	(*e*) [Ne]$3s^13p^1$
(*b*) $1s^22s^22p^1$	(*f*) [Ne]$3s^2$
(*c*) $1s^22s^2$	(*g*) [Xe]$6s^14f^1$
(*d*) [Ar]$4s^13d^1$	(*h*) $1s^12s^1$

2. Write down the spectroscopic-term symbol (^{2S+1}L) for the ground configuration of each of the following: H, He, Li, Na, Be, Mg, Ne, Cl, Cs, Xe, C, N.

3. Draw diagrams of the type of Fig. 5–4 to show that the number of possible J values is $(2L + 1)$ when $S > L$, and $(2S + 1)$ when $L > S$. An example of the former case derives from the configuration d^1; the configuration $1s^12s^1$ exemplifies the latter case.

4. Explain in your own words why the alkali metals do not have spectral lines that can be exactly arranged in a hydrogenic Rydberg series.

5. Why is the energy between two spectroscopic levels not exactly equal to the difference in energy of the configurations from which they stem?

6. Prove that the terms given in the right-hand column below are the only ones that arise from the configurations[a] on the left:

Configuration [a]	Terms
$ns^1(n+1)s^1$	^1S, ^3S
$np^1(n+1)p^1$	^1S, ^1P, ^1D; ^3S, ^3P, ^3D
$nd^1(n+1)d^1$	^1S, ^1P, ^1D, ^1F, ^1G; ^3S, ^3P, ^3D, ^3F, ^3G
ns^2	^1S
np^2	^1S, ^1D, ^3P
nd^2	^1S, ^1D, ^1G, ^3P, ^3F
np^3	^2P, ^2D, ^4S
np^4	^1S, ^1D, ^3P

[a] [n is a principal quantum number; notice the differences in the terms from configurations having inequivalent electrons, e.g., $np^1(n+1)p^1$, and equivalent electrons, e.g., np^2.]

VI

Atomic Excitation Probabilities

THE PREVIOUS CHAPTERS have dealt with properties of individual atoms. On the whole, chemistry is mostly concerned with the properties of collections of atoms and with the details of atomic and molecular interactions. The present chapter, together with Chaps. VII and IX, deals with the nature of certain elementary chemical reactions involving excited atoms. These chapters are intended to familiarize the student with the phenomenological basis of the photophysics and photochemistry of atoms.

6–1 LIFETIMES OF EXCITED STATES

The existence of atomic stationary and levels and the notion that emission lines arise because of transitions or quantum jumps between them immediately raises the question of how long an atom will remain excited before returning to a lower level. The average length of time that an atom spends in a particular state of excitation is measured by the **mean lifetime** of that level.

The probability of a radiative transition occurring between

two levels can be computed from theory. The absorption intensity of the resulting spectral line is a direct experimental measure of that probability. The observed intensity is greatest for those transitions whose computed transition probability is greatest. Since the mean lifetime of an excited level relates to the length of time that the atom remains in that level, and since this time depends on the probability of a downward transition, there must be a relationship between the lifetime and the intensity of the absorption line.

With only two levels in the system, the lifetime of the emission is inversely proportional to the absorption intensity. If a certain number of atoms are excited, and the exciting radiation is suddenly switched off, the emitted intensity will start to decrease in the manner of the curve in Fig. 6–1.

The intensity of emitted light is an observable quantity,

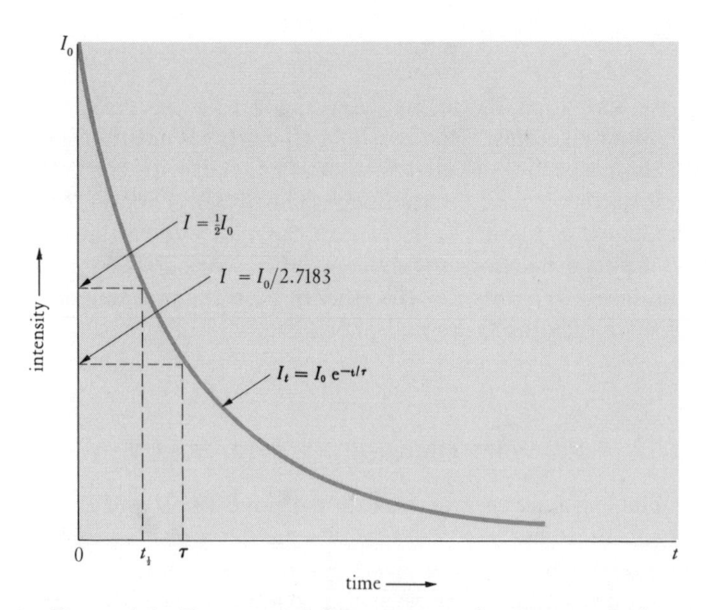

Figure 6–1 Exponential decay curve. At time $t = 0$ the exciting light is extinguished and the intensity decays exponentially with time; i.e., $I = I_0e^{-kt}$, where $k = 1/\tau$.

which at any time relates to the number of excited atoms that are emitting. The actual emission process may be regarded as instantaneous. It is clear from Fig. 6–1 that each atom in the collection does not radiate at the same time. When t is close to zero more quanta per unit time are being emitted than when t is large. Concomitantly, the number of excited atoms in the system decreases as t increases. The lifetime of the excited state of one atom is simply the time that elapses between excitation and emission, each of which is regarded as an instantaneous process. However, experiments are performed on collections of atoms, and it is soon discovered that all the excited atoms do not remain excited for the same period of time; an essentially continuous range of individual 'lifetimes' are observed according to Fig. 6–1. Therefore Fig. 6–1 relates to the probability that a given excited atom will emit in a given time. It remains to define a parameter that is associable with decay curves of this type and which will relate to an average, or most probable, lifetime. There are numerous ways of doing this but the two most common parameters are the **mean lifetime** and the **half-lifetime.**

At zero time the intensity is equal to the value I_0, which is the same as the intensity that was observed under steady illumination. After the mean lifetime has elapsed, the intensity has dropped to exactly $1/e$ of I_0. The relationship between the intensity I_t and the time t is

$$I_t = I_0 e^{-t/\tau} \qquad \textbf{(6–1)}$$

where τ (tau) is the mean lifetime. (A derivation of this equation is given at the end of the summary.) The exponential e has the value 2.7183. Thus when the time τ has elapsed (i.e., when $t = \tau$) we have

$$I_\tau = I_0 e^{-1} = I_0/2.7183 \qquad \textbf{(6–2)}$$

The relationships of Eqs. (6–1) and (6–2) serve to define the mean lifetime τ.

Very often the time characteristic for excited states can be readily measured in terms of the half-life. The half-life $t_{1/2}$ is the time elapsed until the intensity from a collection of excited atoms has dropped to one-half its original value. Thus at $t = t_{1/2}$,

$I_t = (\frac{1}{2})I_0$ and the half-life is related to the lifetime through the equation

$$t_{1/2} = \tau \log_e 2 = 0.693\tau \qquad \textbf{(6–3)}$$

Therefore

$$\tau = 1.44t_{1/2}$$

When there are many lower energy states to which the excited state can undergo transitions, the mean lifetime is dependent on the probabilities of all possible transitions. The student should note that τ and $t_{1/2}$ do not represent different physical processes but are two *defined quantities* used to describe the same physical process.

The Intensities of Spectral Lines

It was indicated in the previous section that the absorption intensity of a spectral line is a direct measure of the probability of the transition between the two states. The absorption spectrum therefore tells us whether a transition is strongly allowed (very intense line), weakly allowed (low-intensity line), or forbidden (extremely weak line compared with the former). The selection rules for atomic spectra are to be regarded as guides toward estimating the intensities of lines rather than as inviolable laws. The selection rules are rigorous only to a *certain degree of approximation.* For example, the spin-intercombination rule ($\Delta S = 0$) is rigorous to the approximation that the spin and orbital motions of the electron can be considered independent. If the spin-orbital interaction is large, the individual quantum numbers L and S are no longer "good quantum numbers." That is, the orbital motion of each electron is influenced by the spin motion, so the orbital or spin angular momenta will not each be constants of the motion. Accordingly separate rules for changes in L and S are no longer rigorous (cf. Sec. 5–5).

The extent to which selection rules can be relaxed is illustrated in Fig. 6–2 in which the log of the ratio of the strength of the lowest singlet-singlet ($n^1S \leftrightarrow n^1P_1$) and singlet-triplet ($n^1S_0 \leftrightarrow n^3P_1$) transitions for various atoms is plotted against the atomic number.

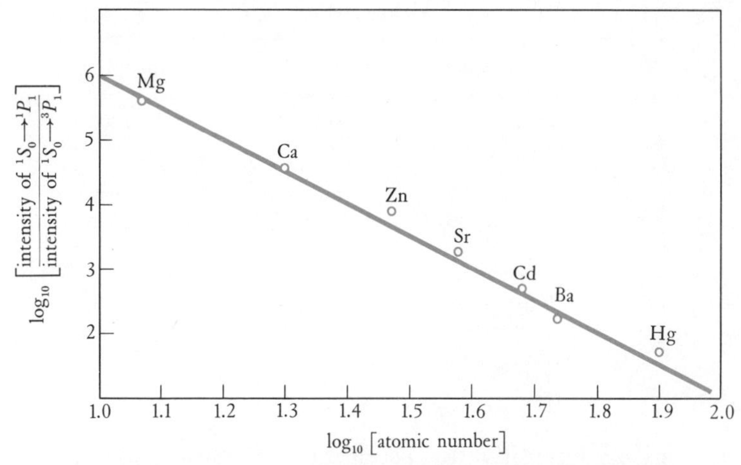

Figure 6–2 A log-log plot illustrating the effect of atomic number on the spin intercombinational-transition probability. The intensity ratio decreases by a factor of 10^5, and the atomic number increases by a factor of 10.

These transitions correspond to the promotion of an electron from a filled *ns* to an *np* orbital. Notice that the intensity ratio is very high for the elements with low atomic number. The plot indicates that the relative intensity for the ${}^1S_0 \leftrightarrow {}^3P_1$ transition increases in proportion to a high power of the atomic number (roughly Z^5 in this case), similar to the manner in which the spin-orbital coupling is expected to increase. For mercury, the ${}^1S_0 \leftrightarrow {}^3P_1$ (2537 A) transition is only 47 times less intense than the spin allowed ${}^1S_0 \leftrightarrow {}^1P_1$ (1894 A) transition, so the former is hardly a forbidden transition. For magnesium the intensity ratio is about $1:10^5$ so in this case the use of the term "forbidden" is more realistic.

Although the selection rules for L and S break down for atoms of large atomic number, the rules for changes in J remain rigorous. Even under large spin-orbital interactions, J remains a good quantum number. The lifetimes of certain transitions for zinc, cadmium, and mercury atoms are listed in Table 6–1. It is of particular interest that the lifetimes of the singlet-singlet transitions

Table 6-1

Atom	Transition	Wavelength, A	Lifetime, sec
Zn	$4^1S_0 \rightarrow 4^1P_1$	2139	5×10^{-8}
	$4^1S_0 \rightarrow 4^3P_1$	3076	1×10^{-5}
Cd	$5^1S_0 \rightarrow 5^1P_1$	2288	2×10^{-9}
	$5^1S_0 \rightarrow 5^3P_1$	3261	2.5×10^{-6}
Hg	$6^1S_0 \rightarrow 6^1P_1$	1849	1.4×10^{-9}
	$6^1S_0 \rightarrow 6^3P_1$	2537	1.1×10^{-7}

are relatively insensitive to the nature of the atom, whereas the singlet-triplet lifetime is about 100 times longer for Zn ($Z = 30$) than for Hg ($Z = 80$). Notice also that the average energy separation between the S and P terms is considerably greater for mercury than for either Zn or Cd. The $S - P$ separation is directly related (note: *not* equal) to the energy separation between the s and p orbitals of the atoms. The unusually large gap between the $6s$ and $6p$ orbitals of Hg is caused by the enhanced shielding of the $6p$ orbitals by the filled $4f$ shell. It is this characteristic that results in extremely weak interatomic forces between Hg atoms and hence in the fact that Hg has an anomalously low melting point.

Metastable Atomic States

A few of the low-lying levels of mercury are shown in Fig. 6-3. The emission processes that can occur are represented as vertical arrows. Since the ground level has $J = 0$ (6^1S_0), transitions to it can only occur from levels with $J = 1$ (the selection rule $\Delta J = 0$, ± 1 excludes transitions between two levels with $J = 0$). The lowest excited level of the atom is 6^3P_0 and transitions to this level from 6^3D_1 and 7^3S_1 are allowed and give rise to the 2967-A and 4047-A emission lines. After the occurrence of either of these transitions, there will be atoms in the 6^3P_0 level. The question now arises as to the fate of these excited atoms. The J selection rule

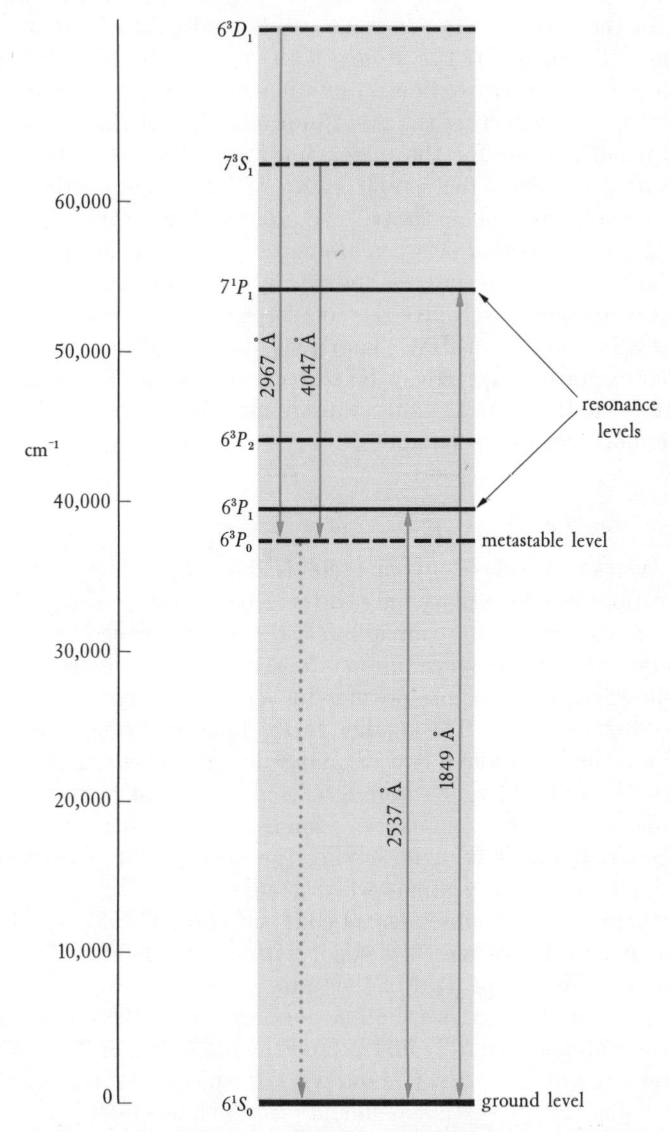

Figure 6–3 A few of the low-lying levels of mercury. The resonance levels are represented as full lines.

forbids the transition to the ground state, and yet there are no intermediate levels. If the atoms in the metastable level are free from external perturbations, radiation of very long lifetime is emitted, thus reflecting the great improbability of the transition. The mean lifetime for the mercury 6^3P_0 level is 1.4×10^{-3} sec. Certain atoms have metastable states with lifetimes on the order of a few seconds. These times—even 10^{-3} sec—are very long compared with the period between atomic collisions in a gas at normal pressures or between atoms and the walls of the gas container. Thus metastable levels give rise to a large variety of secondary reactions in photochemistry. They play the role of *energy sinks* in which excitation energy can be stored and transported from one place to another. Metastable states of molecules are of fundamental importance in bioenergetics.

Resonance Levels

A resonance level of an atom is one from which radiative transitions can take place only to the ground state. Since transitions to the ground state are allowed, the reverse process must also be allowed and resonance lines are observed both in emission and in absorption. It is quite possible for an atom to have more than one resonance level. The alkaline earth atoms, and zinc, cadmium, and mercury each have two resonance levels. These are the two levels $^3P_1$ and $^1P_1$, which were discussed in the last section. It is normal to observe resonance emission from atoms that were previously irradiated with light having the energy of the resonance level. Thus mercury atoms when irradiated with light of wavelength 2537 A will subsequently emit radiation of 2537 A. Similarly, irradiation of mercury vapor with 1849-A light will be followed by emission of light of the same energy.

In later chapters, we shall be concerned with the interactions between atoms. To fully understand the properties of the gaseous systems it will be worthwhile to review the physical theory of classical collisions. The student should read the following section with the aim of developing some feeling for the time and energy scales of interatomic phenomena in gases at normal temperatures and pressures.

6–2 KINETIC THEORY OF GASES

The simple kinetic theory of gases is based on the following assumptions:

1. For any gas of a single substance, all the atoms have the same size and mass.
2. The atoms are not stationary but are in ceaseless random motion during which they may collide with one another or with the walls of the container.
3. The gas *pressure* is caused by the gas atoms colliding against the walls of the container.
4. All the atomic collisions are elastic.
5. At normal pressures the average distance between two atoms is large compared with the size of an atom. Thus we can consider the gas as an assembly of noninteracting particles.
6. The average kinetic energy of the gas atoms is directly related to the temperature of the gas.

The velocity of an atom in a gas is continually changing as the atom participates in collisions during which it can gain or lose kinetic energy. The number of classical collisions between atoms is given by Z, the collision number:

$$Z = 8\left(\frac{\pi k T}{m}\right)^{1/2} r^2 n^2 \text{ collisions/cc/sec} \tag{6–4}$$

where k is the Boltzman constant (1.38×10^{-16} erg/deg/molecule); T is the absolute temperature ($T = 273 + T°\text{C}$); m is the mass of the atom in grams; r is the radius of the atom in centimeters (as defined for example in Sec. 3–3); and n is the number of atoms in 1 cc. For mercury atoms $m = 200 \times 1.67 \times 10^{-24}$ g; $r = 1.44 \times 10^{-8}$ cm; at 25°C the vapor pressure of mercury is about 1.3×10^{-7} atm. At a pressure of 1 atm, 1 mole of gas occupies 22.4 liters; therefore the number of moles in each cubic centimeter at 1.3×10^{-7} atm is

$$n = \frac{1 \times 1.3 \times 10^{-7}}{22.4 \times 1000} = 5.8 \times 10^{-12} \text{ moles/cc}$$

Since 1 mole consists of 6.03×10^{23} molecules (Avogadro's number), n is $5.8 \times 10^{-12} \times 6.03 \times 10^{23} = 3.5 \times 10^{12}$ molecules/cc. Thus the number of collisions each second in every cubic centimeter is

$$Z = 8\left(\frac{3.14 \times 1.38 \times 10^{-16} \times 298}{200 \times 1.67 \times 10^{-24}}\right)^{1/2} \times (3.5 \times 10^{-12})^2 \times (1.44 \times 10^{-8})^2$$

Therefore

$$Z = 7.8 \times 10^{14} \text{ collisions/cc/sec}$$

It is useful to calculate Z in terms of the number of collisions made by each molecule per second. To obtain this result we divide the above Z by the number of molecules in 1 cc. The new collision number Z' is given by

$$Z' = \frac{7.8 \times 10^{14}}{3.5 \times 10^{12}} = 2.23 \times 10^2 \text{ collisions/molecule/sec}$$

Since there are 2.23×10^2 collisions/sec, the average time between collisions is $1/Z' = 4.5 \times 10^{-3}$ sec. If the gas pressure is raised to 1 atm (i.e., the pressure of mercury vapor above boiling mercury at 356°C), the value of Z becomes 2.76×10^{28} collisions/sec/cc and Z' is equal to 1.03×10^9 collisions/sec/molecule. Thus at the higher pressure the average time between classical collisions is about 10^{-9} sec.

The mean lifetime of an excited atom is usually about 10^{-8} sec; therefore each excited atom can undergo about ten classical collisions during its lifetime. At low pressures (10^{-6} atm) excited atoms with mean lifetimes of 10^{-8} sec will most probably not suffer any classical collisions—about 1 excited atom in 10^5 will undergo a collision. For metastable excited states the number of collisions can be extremely large. Thus in the vapor of boiling mercury, each metastable excited atom ($\tau = 10^{-5}$ sec) will collide about 10^4 times during the mean lifetime (however see p. 115 regarding what is meant by a collision).

The importance of excited states in gas-phase chemical reactions is principally due to the fact that the lifetimes of those states are comparable to the durations between successive collisions. Chemical or physical changes may occur during the collisions.

Therefore excited atoms are able to react with other atoms if their lifetimes are long compared with the collision period.

Steady-State Excitation

The question now arises as to the number of atoms in an irradiated gas that are actually in an excited state at any time.

Suppose that light of intensity I is totally absorbed by the gas. The intensity of electromagnetic radiation is conveniently measured in terms of the number of quanta produced in each second. Ordinary room lights emit about 10^{13} quanta/sec of visible radiation; powerful arcs emit about 10^{20} quanta/sec. Each quantum of the appropriate energy can usually be utilized to excite just one atom. Let us choose a light source of intermediate intensity such that

$$I = 10^{15} \text{ quanta/sec/cm}^2$$

The area of the face of the gas cell is 1 cm², so the rate of light absorption is 10^{15} quanta/sec, if there is enough gas for all the incident light to be absorbed in a cell length of 1 cm (see Fig. 6–4). Let the gas pressure be 1 atm at 25°C. Once the light has been

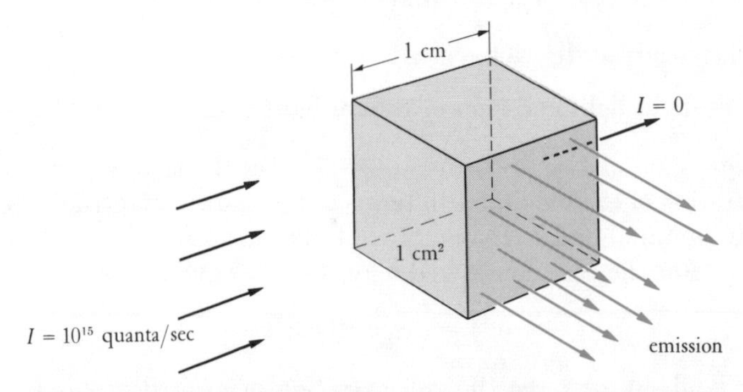

Figure 6–4 Schematic of total absorption of light by a cube of gas. (Most of the emissions originate from the incident surface, as this is the region where most of the light is absorbed. The emission is isotropic.)

switched on for some time, *the rate of light absorption is equal to the rate of light emission.* This condition defines what is known as the **steady state**—there is no net change, with time, of the number of excited atoms.

The rate at which light is emitted from the irradiated gas is proportional to the number of atoms that are excited. Suppose the number of excited atoms in 1 cc equals $[c^*]$; then,

$$\text{rate of light emission} = k[c^*] \qquad (6\text{–}5)$$

where the proportionality constant k is the rate of light emission when $[c^*]$ is equal to precisely one excited atom per cc. Placing $[c^*] = 1$, we find that

$$\text{rate of light emission} = k \text{ quanta/sec/cc}$$

Since k measures the number of quanta that are emitted in every second from 1/cc of gas, the reciprocal of k must relate to the time between the emission of successive quanta. Thus $1/k$ is just the mean time that excitation energy resides in the volume of gas. It follows that k and τ are in reciprocal relationship:

$$\tau = 1/k \qquad (6\text{–}6)$$

Equation (6–5) can now be written

$$\text{rate of light emission} = k[c^*] = [c^*]/\tau \qquad (6\text{–}7)$$

In the steady state we have

$$\text{rate of light emission} = \text{rate of light absorption} = I \qquad (6\text{–}8)$$

Substitution of Eq. (6–7) in Eq. (6–8) gives the steady-state concentration of excited atoms in terms of the known quantities τ (the mean lifetime) and I (the number of quanta absorbed in each second). For the case considered here, $I = 10^{15}$ quanta/sec/cc; thus

$$[c^*] = 10^{15}\tau \text{ atoms/cc}$$

If τ is about 10^{-8} sec the concentration of excited atoms is 10^7 molecules/cc. The total number of atoms in the cell will be of the order of 10^{18} at a pressure of 1 atm in a volume of 10^{-3} liter. Thus the ratio of unexcited to excited atoms is $10^{18}/10^7 = 10^{11}:1$.

For states that are not metastable, the number of excited atoms is extremely small compared with the number of unexcited atoms. Consequently collisions between the excited atoms are extremely improbable. On the other hand collisions between metastable atoms are not so improbable if the mean lifetimes of the metastable levels are about 1 sec.

6–3 SUMMARY

1. The mean lifetime of an atomic resonance level is inversely proportional to the intensity of the absorption to that level.

2. The mean lifetime is the time after which the emission intensity falls to $1/e$ of its original value. The half-life elapses when the original intensity drops by one-half.

3. The emission intensity from a collection of atoms decays according to an exponential law,

$$I_t = I_0 e^{-t/\tau}$$

This equation is equivalent to

$$\log_e \frac{I_0}{I_t} = \frac{t}{\tau}$$

thus a plot of t vs. $\log_e (I_0/I_t)$ should be linear with the slope of the line equal to $1/\tau$.

4. In general the mean lifetime of an upper state is dependent on the probabilities of all possible transitions from that state to lower states.

5. Selection rules are not yes-or-no regulations. Primarily, the simple selection rules involve some degree of approximation, and they may be violated under the influence of previously neglected interactions. For example the rule $\Delta S = 0$ is not rigorous if spin-orbital coupling occurs.

6. Levels that cannot spontaneously revert to a lower level because of selection rules are metastable. They have longer lifetimes than levels from which transitions are allowed.

7. Resonance radiation originates from levels that combine directly with the ground level but not with intermediate levels.

They are usually allowed transitions that can be observed in absorption as well as emission.

8. The distribution of velocities in gaseous systems leads to an average number of classical collisions Z:

$$Z = 8\left(\frac{\pi kT}{m}\right)^{1/2} \tau^2 n^2 \text{ collisions/cc/sec}$$

From this formula it was shown that an atom with a classical radius in a gas at 1 atm pressure undergoes about 10^9 collisions/sec.

9. The collision number is of the same order of magnitude as the mean lifetimes of allowed levels; thus during their lifetime excited atoms are able to collide with other atoms.

10. Atoms in metastable levels (having as much as 5 to 10 eV of excitation energy) can undergo hundreds of collisions during the excited-state lifetime.

11. Irradiated systems very soon reach a steady-state condition where the number of light quanta absorbed in each second is equal to the number of quanta emitted in every second. If more than one event can occur after excitation (e.g., two emissions or photochemical reactions), there is no net change with time in the steady state in the number of excited atoms. Thus the steady-state concentration of primary excited atoms is still equal to the rate of light absorption multiplied by the mean lifetime of the excited atoms. Of course in this event the mean life will not be as simple as in paragraph 3.

12. (By way of an appendix) the derivation [from the rate law (6–5)] of the intensity-decay law, which goes into effect when the exciting light is switched off, requires the use of simple calculus. The rate law states that the rate of emission is equal to a constant k times the number of excited species $[c^*]$. The rate of emission is the rate at which the concentration of excited species decreases $-d[c^*]/dt$. Thus

$$-\frac{d[c^*]}{dt} = k[c^*] \qquad (6\text{–}9)$$

Therefore

$$\frac{d[c^*]}{[c^*]} = -k\,dt \qquad (6\text{–}10)$$

Integration of Eq. (6–10) from $[c^*] = [c^*]_0$ to $[c^*]_t$ and $t = 0$ to t gives

$$\log_e \left(\frac{[c^*]_t}{[c^*]_0}\right) = -kt$$

Taking antilogs yields

$$[c^*]_t = [c^*]_0 e^{-kt}$$

The ratio $[c^*]_t/[c^*]_0$ is equal to the ratio I_t/I_0. We can replace $[c^*]_t$, the number of excited species left at time t, by I_t, and replace $[c^*]_0$, the number in the steady state before switching off the exciting source, by I_0. Hence we obtain Eq. (6–1). Notice that k, the rate constant, is a reciprocal time, i.e.,

$$k = 1/\tau \text{ sec}^{-1}$$

We can set up the steady-state condition in the following manner: The net rate of formation of excited species is zero at the steady state. Thus

$$\frac{d[c^*]}{dt} = 0$$

However, $d[c^*]/dt$ is equal to the rate of light absorption I *less* the rate of emission, hence

$$\frac{d[c^*]}{dt} = I - k[c^*] = I - \frac{[c^*]}{\tau} = 0$$

Therefore

$$I = [c^*]/\tau \qquad \textbf{(6–11)}$$

which is identical with Eq. (6–8).

PROBLEMS

1. During an emission experiment the exciting light is suddenly extinguished; the intensity drops to half its original value after 6.0×10^{-4} sec. Calculate the mean life of the emission. What is the major assumption in this calculation?

2. The resonance emission from a gas has a half-life of 8×10^{-5} sec. If the exciting radiation is absorbed to the extent of

5×10^{17} quanta $\sec^{-1}$ cc^{-1}, what is the steady-state concentration of excited atoms in the gas? What is the concentration of excited atoms after the exciting light has been extinguished for 8×10^{-6} sec?

3. Calculate the apparent radius of sodium atoms that were found to undergo 10^{13} collisions/cc/sec, at a temperature of 25°C and pressure 2×10^{-7} atm. What is the physical significance of this value? Why is your answer not 1.57 A, which is the normally accepted covalent radius of sodium?

4. A gaseous system contains three simultaneously emitting species A^*, B^*, and C^*; in the steady state the relative excited-state concentrations are $[A^*]:[B^*]:[C^*] = 5:2:1$. What are the relative concentrations when $[A^*]$ has dropped to half of its value ($\tau_{A^*} = 5 \times 10^{-8}$, $\tau_{B^*} = 2 \times 10^{-8}$, $\tau_{C^*} = 1 \times 10^{-8}$ sec)?

VII

Collision Processes Involving Excited Atoms

In the previous chapter the kinematics of collisions was described but no mention was made of the detailed nature of the collision process. When we try to elaborate on this point we are immediately faced with the problem of how close two atoms must approach to produce a collision. To answer this question for classical particles presents no difficulty—the colliding particles simply must touch one another. However, the charge cloud of an electron in an atom does not have a definite boundary, and the electron has a small probability of being located very distant from the atom. Furthermore, the idea of atomic particles with known kinetic energy moving in definite paths must be rejected on the grounds of the uncertainty principle. Thus the charge clouds of atoms can 'touch' even when the atomic nuclei are far apart. We therefore define a **cross section** for atomic collisions which can be larger than expected on the basis that atoms behave like rigid spheres of radius equal to the atomic radius.[1]

[1] The atomic radius is an arbitrary measure of atomic size. The usual values refer to one-half the distance between the centers of atoms that are close-packed in a crystal lattice. There is absolutely no reason to expect radii measured in this fashion to relate to collisional cross sections in gases.

The effective cross-sectional area (or volume) for an atom is the area (or volume) that the atom appears to occupy on the basis of applying classical theory to experimental measurements of the number of collisions. We would not expect that an atom would interact in exactly the same manner with an electron as it would with another atom; nor would the interaction with one atom be the same as with other atoms. Consequently the effective cross section will depend on which process is under consideration; thus we shall refer to the cross section for a *particular* process. The cross section will depend on the relative velocities of the colliding particles and hence will vary with temperature. By the same token, the effective cross section for collisions between atoms and slow electrons will be very different from that for collisions with fast electrons.

The sphere of interaction of an atom is not simply its covalent radius. The effective cross section for a process is the ratio of the experimental number of collisions (per second per cubic centimeter) to the number calculated from kinetic theory assuming that the atoms have unit effective diameter. If two different atoms are involved in the process the effective cross section σ^2 can be obtained from the equation

$$\text{experimental number of collisions} = 2n_1n_2\sigma^2\left[2\pi kT\left(\frac{1}{m_1}+\frac{1}{m_2}\right)\right]^{1/2}$$

where n_1 and n_2 are the concentrations of the two species, m_1 and m_2 are their masses, k is the Boltzmann constant, and T is the absolute temperature. The term σ is identifiable with the effective diameter of the colliding species; i.e., the average distance between their centers when the collision occurs [cf. Eq. (6–4)]. The effective cross section σ can become much less than the classical gas-kinetic radius. This means that not every collision need be effective in bringing about the reaction under consideration.

In Chap. II the inelastic collisions between electrons and atoms were discussed, and it was found that electron kinetic energy could be utilized to electronically excite an atom. It is also possible to electronically excite an atom by utilizing the energy of another excited atom. This process is known as **energy transfer** or photosensitization; and often occurs with extremely large cross section. In other words excitation energy can be transferred from one atom to another even when the two atoms are very far apart. In this chapter we shall examine in detail some of the experiments that have provided the background for modern ideas of energy transfer.

7–1 SENSITIZED FLUORESCENCE

Consider a gas consisting of two different kinds of atoms. Assume that we know the complete absorption and emission spectra of the two components of the mixture. The mixture is now irradiated with light that can only be absorbed by *one of the components*. In certain cases the resulting fluorescence contains lines either from both components or exclusively from the atoms that did not absorb the radiation in the first place. Luminescence of this type is called sensitized fluorescence. This name connotes the fact that the fluorescence is not caused by direct optical excitation but by some secondary process that involves the participation of another excited species. The observation of sensitized fluorescence provides a direct confirmation of the concept of energy transfer, and it also provides an experimental tool that can be used to obtain precise details of collisional and energy-transfer processes. In such experiments it is customary to refer to the atoms as either **excitation-energy donors** or **excitation-energy acceptors,** based on whether they are the primary absorbers or the ultimate emitters.

Preliminary experiments with a variety of donors and acceptors show that the essential criterion for the occurrence of energy transfer is that the donor atoms have an electronic level which has a similar or greater energy than that of the ultimate excited level of the acceptor atoms. For example, it should be possible on an energy basis to transfer energy from atoms of type A (see Fig. 7–1) to those of type B. It should not be possible to excite atom C with the electronic excitation energy of atom A.

One of the earliest quantitative energy-transfer experiments was performed by Franck and Cario (1922) in which a mixture of mercury and thallium was examined. A quartz tube containing thallium and mercury vapors was heated to 800°C and irradiated

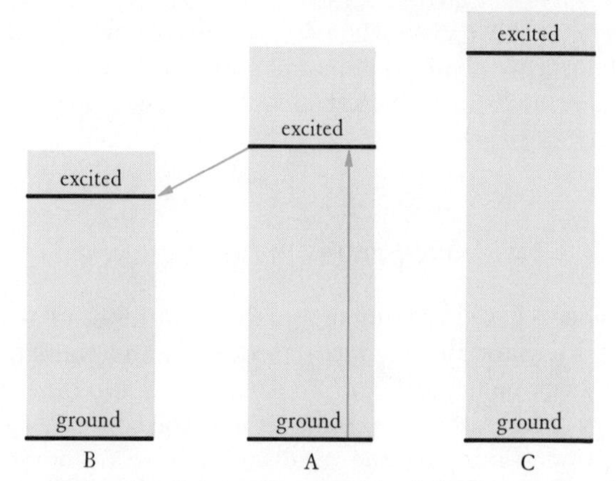

Figure 7–1 Conditions for sensitized fluorescence. Energy transfer is possible from A to B but not from A to C under normal circumstances.

with the 2537-A mercury resonance line from a mercury arc. Light of this wavelength *is not absorbed by thallium atoms.* The emission spectrum of the mixed vapor was found to contain many thallium lines. Later experiments on mercury vapor both in the presence and absence of thallium showed that the total intensity of sensitized fluorescence was equal to the decrease in intensity of mercury fluorescence. A few of the energy levels of thallium are shown in Fig. 7–2. Its ground configuration is like that of mercury plus one $6p$ electron and its normal spectrum is due to this extra electron, the remainder being in filled shells or filled subshells. The configuration $[\mathrm{Hg}]6p^1$ gives rise to two levels $^2P_{1/2}$ and $^2P_{3/2}$, of which $^2P_{1/2}$ is lowest in energy and therefore the ground level of the atom. The $^2P_{3/2}$ level lies nearly 1 eV above ground, and the $7^2S_{1/2}$ and $6^2D_{3/2}$ levels are about 3.3 and 4.5 eV above the ground level, respectively. Each of the transitions $6^2D_{3/2} \rightarrow 6^2P_{1/2}$, $6^2P_{3/2}$ and $7^2S_{1/2} \rightarrow 6^2P_{1/2}$, $6^2P_{3/2}$ are allowed and each is observed in the sensitized-fluorescence experiment. Notice that 4.9 eV [the energy of the mercury $^3P_1$ (2537-A level)] is sufficient to excite each of these thallium levels.

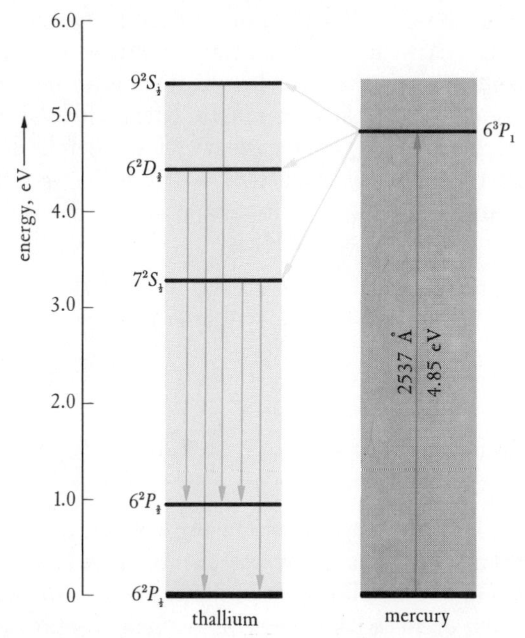

Figure 7–2 Energy transfer from mercury to thallium.

The energy levels of mercury and thallium are not identical so the energies cannot exactly match. We must now enquire about the fate of the excess energy after the energy-transfer process has occurred. For example, suppose energy is transferred from a mercury atom in the 6^3P_1 (4.85-eV) level to an unexcited thallium atom such that the thallium ends up in the $6^2D_{3/2}$ (4.45-eV) level. The excess of energy is 0.40 eV, and this is not sufficient to bring about electronic excitation to any electronic level of either mercury or thallium. Since the total energy of the system must be conserved it was concluded that the excess of energy is taken up as translational kinetic energy of the atoms. The reverse process can also be confirmed by observations of sensitized fluorescence. For example, the sensitized spectrum shows the 2826-A line due to the $9^2S_{1/2} \rightarrow 6^2P_{3/2}$ transition of thallium.

The $9^2S_{1/2}$ level (5.36 eV) could not possibly become excited through collisions with mercury atoms unless some energy other than electronic energy was available. The extra 0.51 eV can be obtained by converting atomic kinetic energy into electronic excitation energy. The dynamic theory of gases tells us that the average kinetic energy of gas atoms is $\frac{3}{2}kT$, where k is the Boltzmann constant and T the absolute temperature. Thus the average kinetic energy at 800°C (1073°K) is

$$\begin{aligned} \text{average kinetic energy} &= 1.5 \times 1.38 \times 10^{-16} \times 1073 \text{ erg/molecule} \\ &= 2.24 \times 10^{-13} \text{ erg/molecule} \end{aligned}$$

and since

$$\begin{aligned} 1 \text{ erg/molecule} &= 6.24 \times 10^{11} \text{ eV} \\ \text{average kinetic energy} &= 6.24 \times 2.24 \times 10^{-2} \text{ eV} \\ &= 0.13 \text{ eV} \end{aligned}$$

Since it is the average kinetic energy which is 0.13 eV, many atoms will have either more or less energy than this. A detailed examination of the distribution of kinetic energies about the average shows that atoms with 0.51 eV are sufficiently prevalent under the experimental conditions to account for the intensity of the observed spectral lines. As we expected, the sensitized lines from levels higher than 4.85 eV are weaker than those from the lower levels, and intensity of emission from the higher-energy levels decreases with decreasing temperature. From the above experimental results it is possible to derive the cross section for energy transfer in such systems. As a rule it is found that the average distance between the donor and acceptor atoms for energy transfer to occur is about 8 to 20 A, which corresponds to from three to six atomic covalent radii.

Collisions with Metastable Atoms

The student will realize that the study of resonance radiation, and the efficiency of energy transfer resulting in sensitized fluorescence, provide very useful methods of obtaining information about collision processes in gases. Much of the early information on this topic came from studies of the inert gases He, Ne, Ar, Kr, and Xe. We shall discuss the case of He in some detail.

Helium has the configuration $1s^2$ and the ground level is 1^1S_0. The two electrons can have their spins unpaired in the configuration $1s^12s^1$ corresponding to the state $^3S_0$. Analysis of the helium spectrum leads to *two essentially independent systems of terms*, owing to singlet-singlet and triplet-triplet transitions. The intercombination selection rules are rigorously upheld to such an extent that once the lowest triplet level is populated, say, in a discharge tube, its lifetime is determined by the rate at which excited atoms diffuse to the walls of the tube. Under normal conditions no radiation corresponding to the transition $^3S_1 \rightarrow {}^1S_0$ is observed. Thus in a helium discharge tube there are essentially two "ground levels" within the time scale of normal experimentation. The first is the true ground level $^1S_0$, and the other is the highly metastable $^3S_1$ level. Certain other levels are shown in Fig. 7–3. During electric excitation, a significant concentration of atoms in the $^3S_1$ level is established. These can be detected by measurements of the *absorption* $^3S_1 \rightarrow n^3P$. When the electrical power is turned off the intensity of absorption, $^3S_1 \rightarrow {}^3P$, decreases slowly as the $^3S_1$ excited atoms disappear by diffusing to the walls of the vessel where they lose their excitation energy. The rate of decrease of absorption intensity therefore relates directly to the lifetime of the $^3S_1$ excited state. The lifetime depends entirely on the efficiency of diffusion of excited atoms to the walls of the vessel; thus the experimental results provide detailed information of the processes that metastable atoms undergo after the excitation has been removed.

Analogous experiments have been carried out with argon. Electric excitation causes the production of the metastable $^3P_2$ level (see Fig. 7–4). A sufficiently large number of excited atoms is produced making it possible to examine the absorption spectrum with $^3P_2$ as the base level. The manner in which this absorption intensity decreases with time after the electric power is switched off provides information about collision processes. The observed lifetimes for decay of absorption intensity are found to be around 10^{-3} sec. These values are in substantial agreement with calculations based on the kinetic theory of gases.

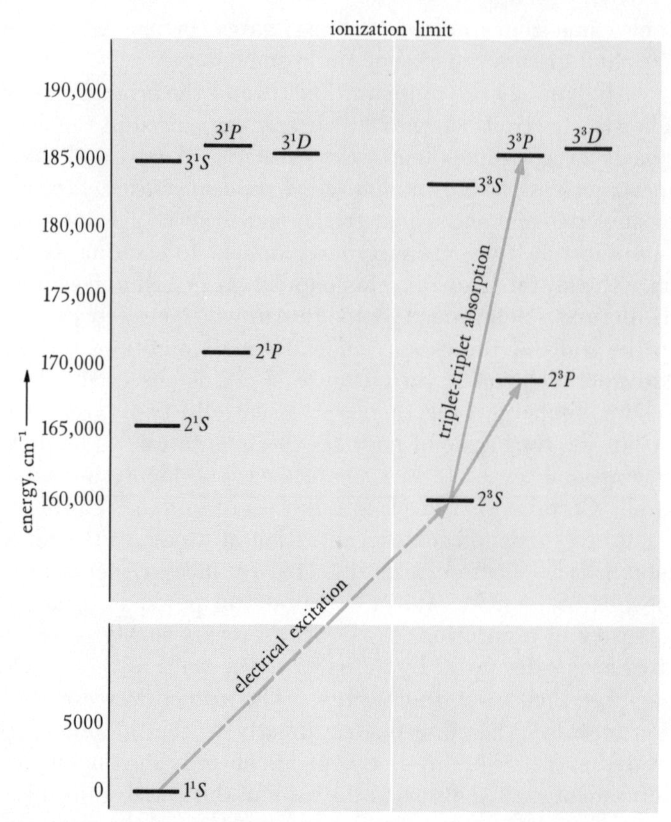

Figure 7–3 Term diagram for helium. The terms with principal quantum numbers 4, 5, 6, . . . , etc., are compressed into the region below the ionization limit.

7–2 ENERGY RESONANCE

Quantum mechanics predicts that the maximum interaction between two atoms occurs when their states are at the same energy. Two states at exactly the same energy are said to be *in resonance.* When the states are close in energy they are in *near resonance.* The efficiency of energy transfer between atoms de-

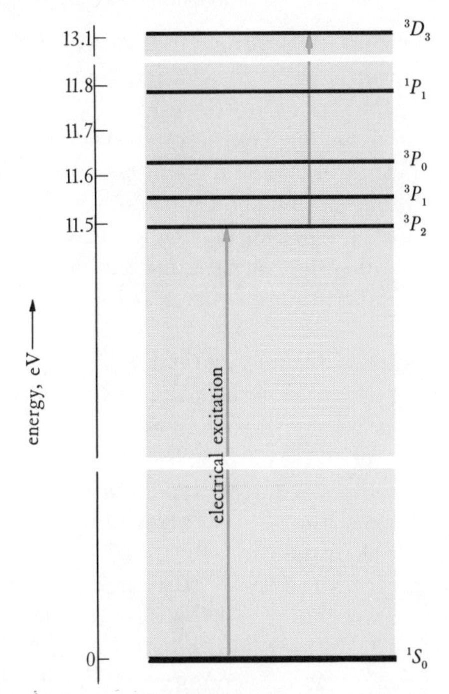

Figure 7–4 Some low-lying states of argon.

pends on the strength of their mutual interaction, which is intimately associated with the proximity of their energy states. At near resonance the probability of energy transfer from atom D in energy state E_D, to atom A in energy state E_A, is inversely proportional to the energy difference $(E_D - E_A)$:

$$\text{probability of energy transfer} \propto 1/E_D - E_A$$

In view of these conclusions, the most efficient energy-transfer processes should occur between identical atoms. The experimental verification of this involves the measurement of the polarization of the radiation from atoms in short-lived states. Atoms that are excited with plane-polarized light will emit plane-polarized light under certain experimental conditions.[1] However if the assembly of atoms undergoes considerable fluctuation before the absorbed energy is reemitted, the radiation will appear depolarized. We know from kinetic theory that the collision frequency is small compared with the mean lifetime of emission if the gas pressure is low. Thus collisions and atomic motion should not upset the polarization of atomic radiation at low pressures. However it is found that the emission is considerably depolarized, and this is taken as direct evidence for the efficient transfer of energy between atoms of the same kind.

The importance of the energy relationship in determining the efficiency of energy transfer is beautifully illustrated in the mercury-sensitized fluorescence of sodium vapor. As a rule the intensities of lines in a series (say $nD \rightarrow 3P$) decrease with increasing principal quantum number in the upper state. Thus in the spectrum of sodium atoms, the $9S \rightarrow 3P$ transitions (see Fig. 7–5) are very much weaker than the $6S \rightarrow 3P$ or $7S \rightarrow 3P$ transitions. In the sensitized spectrum the $9S \rightarrow 3P$ transitions are the most intense in the series, and the $7S \rightarrow 3P$ is also unusually strong. The most intense $D \rightarrow 3P$ transition originates from $7D$, which is extremely close in energy to the mercury-6^3P_1 level. Thus by comparing the relative intensities of lines in the normal sodium emission with those in the sensitized spectrum, one concludes that proximity of donor and acceptor states increases the probability of energy transfer. The energy transfer can be represented by a chemical equation as follows:

$$\mathrm{Hg}^*(6^3P_1) + \mathrm{Na} \rightarrow \mathrm{Hg} + \mathrm{Na}^*(7^2D_{3/2})$$

where the asterisks indicate an excited state.

The effective radii of the atoms for energy transfer can be calculated from this intensity data. The values obtained for these

[1] The proper experimental conditions may require a weak magnetic field. In Chap. VIII it will be shown that each J level is made up of $(2J + 1)$ closely spaced states characterized by the quantum number M_J. The polarization of an atomic transition depends on M_J. In a weak magnetic field the M_J state of the atom is in near resonance with the $M_J'(\neq M_J)$ state of another atom. Thus energy transfer is efficient and the polarization of the luminescence is affected.

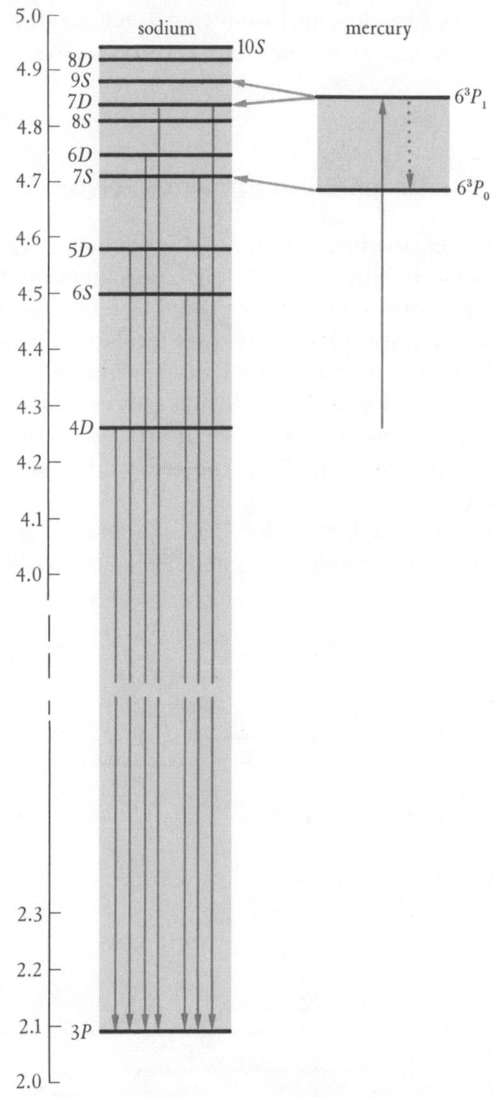

Figure 7–5 The importance of resonance in nonradiative energy transfer: the transfer of electronic excitation from mercury to sodium. The strong lines in the sodium emission spectrum originate from the three states 9*S*, 7*D*, and 7*S*, which are closest to the mercury resonance levels.

effective radii lead to the conclusion that the excitation energy is transferred by means of a nonradiative process over very large distances.

7-3 INTERCONVERSIONS BETWEEN ATOMIC LEVELS

We have said previously that the lifetime of an excited level depends on the probability of all the processes an excited atom can undergo. In normal circumstances the only events that may occur are spontaneous quantum jumps to lower levels giving rise to emission lines. We have also seen that atomic kinetic energy is interconvertible with electronic excitation energy during collisions involving energy transfer. Now we must ask whether certain transitions that are not normally permitted can be caused to occur during collisions.

The two lowest excited levels of the sodium atom are shown in Fig. 7-6. Each of the levels $3^2P_{1/2}$ and $3^2P_{3/2}$ can undergo transi-

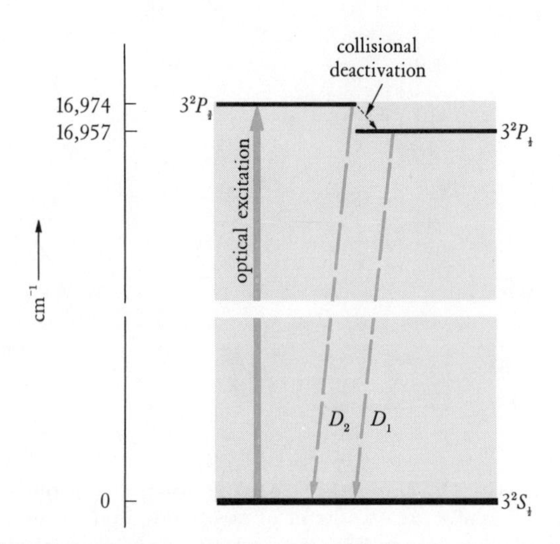

Figure 7-6 Demonstration of collisional deactivation. The sodium state $^2P_{3/2}$ is selectively excited.

tions with the ground level, $3^2S_{1/2}$, both in absorption and emission (the sodium D-lines; see Sec. 5–5). The separation between the ^2P levels is 17 cm^{-1}. We require an experiment in which only one of the upper levels is excited in order to observe whether one or both of the sodium-D lines appear in the emission spectrum.

The light from a sodium lamp is passed through a prism and the dispersed light made to fall on a narrow slit. The dispersion is such that only one of the D-lines can pass through the slit. The higher energy line, due to the transition $3^2P_{3/2} \rightarrow 3^2S_{1/2}$, is allowed to pass through the slit and is directed into a chamber of sodium vapor at a known temperature and pressure. The light is absorbed and some sodium atoms are raised to the $3^3P_{3/2}$ level. The emission originating from the vapor is collected by a spectrograph and photographed. Except when the sodium pressure is very low, both sodium-D lines appear in the emission spectrum. If an inert gas such as argon is mixed with the sodium vapor, both D-lines appear in the spectrum even if the sodium pressure is very low. When the sodium pressure is above 10^{-6} atm, the two D-lines are always present in the spectrum. Thus the following reactions can occur:

$$\mathrm{Na}^*_{(1)}(3^2P_{3/2}) + \mathrm{Na}_{(2)} \rightarrow \mathrm{Na}_{(1)} + \mathrm{Na}^*_{(2)}(3^2P_{1/2}) \qquad \textbf{(7–1)}$$

$$\mathrm{Na}^*(3^2P_{3/2}) + \mathrm{Ar} \rightarrow \mathrm{Na}^*(3^2P_{1/2}) + \mathrm{Ar} \qquad \textbf{(7–2)}$$

In Eq. (7–1) the original excited and unexcited atoms are distinguished by subscripts (1) and (2), respectively. Reaction (7–2) involves *collisional deactivation* of the $^2P_{3/2}$ state, the excess of electronic energy being converted to kinetic energy of the particles. The reaction in (7–1) involves energy transfer from atom (1) to atom (2) and again the energy balance is maintained by a gain in the kinetic energy of the atoms after collision. It should be noted that the transition $3^2P_{3/2} \rightarrow 3^2P_{1/2}$ is forbidden, since the selection rule $\Delta L = \pm 1$ would be violated. Thus radiative transitions between these two levels cannot occur with high probability. The reactions in Eqs. (7–1) and (7–2) each correspond to nonradiative transitions. The effective cross section for conversion between the two states is about 200 times greater for the process of (7–1) than for the process of (7–2), once again illustrating the extremely efficient nature of long-range energy transfer when the donor and acceptor states are at similar energies.

Comparable experiments have been performed with mercury vapor in which the 6^3P_1 (2537-A) level is preferentially excited. In the presence of foreign gases or at high mercury pressures the lower-energy metastable 6^3P_0 level becomes populated. The presence of this excited level can be proven by simultaneously observing the absorption at 2967 A, which corresponds to the $6^3P_0 \rightarrow 6^3D$ transition (see Fig. 6–3). The technique in this experiment is similar to that of the helium experiments described in the last section and is generally referred to as metastable-state absorption spectroscopy.

In recent years it has become possible to detect and study the absorption spectra of relatively short-lived states by using rapid-flash sources of excitation. The source of excitation is an intense flash of duration about 10^{-7} sec. This flash triggers a second flash that is of low intensity and passes through the recently excited gas into the spectrograph. It may be arranged that the second flash, which records an absorption spectrum on the plate, occurs about 10^{-6} sec after excitation. Thus species and events that have mean lifetimes on this time scale may be studied in some detail.

7–4 THE ASSOCIATION OF EXCITED AND UNEXCITED ATOMS

It is well known that certain species have stable monatomic forms, e.g., the inert gases. The halogens, F, Cl, Br, and I, are most stable as the diatomic molecules F_2, Cl_2, Br_2. These designations refer to the ground-state atoms. Thus helium is monatomic in its ground state, and ground-state chlorine atoms normally form diatomic molecules. The chemical reactions between normal helium atoms and between normal chlorine atoms can be described by the following equations:

no reaction $\quad \mathrm{He}(^1S_0) + \mathrm{He}(^1S_0) \rightarrow \mathrm{He}(^1S_0) + \mathrm{He}(^1S_0)$

reaction[1] $\quad \mathrm{Cl}(^2P) + \mathrm{Cl}(^2P) \rightarrow \mathrm{Cl{-}Cl}$

---

[1] Using the methods of Chap. V it is possible to deduce the terms arising from the normal configuration of Cl, $[\mathrm{Ne}](3s^2)3p^5$. However with five equivalent electrons the treatment is lengthy and difficult. When a subshell is more than half-filled, the terms are easily obtained by considering the "holes" in the

The identical situation may not hold when one of the atoms is in an excited state. Indeed it is found that many normally monatomic vapors form diatomic species when irradiated. For example for helium:

$$\mathrm{He}(^1S_0) + \mathrm{He}(2^3S_1) \rightarrow (\mathrm{He{-}He})^*$$

Notice that the molecule is excited (as indicated by the asterisk), since if it were not, the species could not exist as a diatomic molecule but would be equivalent to two separated atoms. Such species that are stable only in excited states are often called excimers. They are detected by their emission spectra, which resemble molecular spectra (they have in fact continuous emission spectra) in having no atomic line characteristics. Excimers play an important part in many atomic collision processes. In particular they are intermediates in certain reactions concerned with photoionization.

When cesium vapor is irradiated with the energy appropriate to cause the $6^2S_{1/2} \rightarrow n^2P$ transitions, free electrons are produced in the gas. Since the excitation is absorbed into bound levels of the type n^2P where $n = 6, 7, 8, 9, \ldots$, etc., it is certain that the ionization limit is not attained by direct excitation. Furthermore, the energy gap between the ionization limit and the states 8^2P or 9^2P is too great (about 0.3 eV), under the conditions of the experiment, to account for the observed efficiency of ionization by collisional kinetic energy alone (see Fig. 7–7). According to the accepted point of view, the ionization takes place in two steps. The first involves the formation of an excimer

$$\mathrm{Cs}^*(n^2P) + \mathrm{Cs} \rightarrow (\mathrm{Cs{-}Cs})^*$$

The level of excitation of the molecule is such that it is above its ionization limit, and an electron is immediately ejected:

$$(\mathrm{Cs{-}Cs})^* \rightarrow (\mathrm{Cs{-}Cs})^+ + \text{electron}$$

In the presence of inert gases the photoionization efficiency is very much reduced. This is explained on the basis of the occur-

---

subshell rather than the electrons. The techniques are identical to those given in Chap. V with the energy relationships between the terms just the reverse of those for electrons. Thus [Cl]$3p^5$ is treated as a p^1 configuration with $L = 1$, $J = \frac{1}{2}$ or $\frac{3}{2}$ and the two levels $^2P_{1/2}$ and $^2P_{3/2}$ arise. Similarly p^4 gives ^1S ^3P, and ^1D terms (cf. p^2).

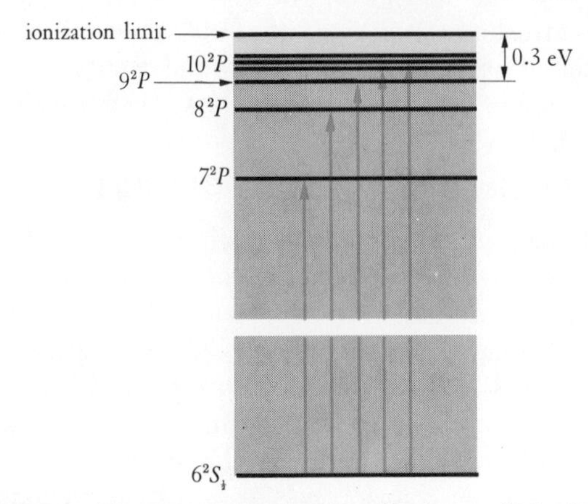

Figure 7–7 Energy states, series limit, and ionization continuum for cesium atoms.

rence of collisions of the type presented in Eq. (7–2), which were discussed in the last section.

Collisions of Excited Atoms with Molecules

Excited atoms can lose their electronic excitation energy much more efficiently during collisions with certain molecules than with other atoms. This is because the electronic energy can be transferred into energy of vibrational motion of the molecule. Since molecules have a large number of vibrational energy states with energies of a few tenths of an electron volt, the conditions for resonance transfer of excitation energy are often readily met.

In certain cases the collision between an excited atom and a molecule can lead to a chemical reaction, such as the dissociation or ionization of the molecule. When hydrogen molecules interact with excited mercury atoms, hydrogen atoms result. The mercury atoms are originally in the 6^3P_1 level and the hydrogen molecules are in their ground state. The first step in the reaction is the collision between the two species:

$$\mathrm{Hg}^*(6^3P_1) + \mathrm{H{-}H} \rightarrow (\mathrm{Hg{-}H})^* + \mathrm{H}$$

There results a hydrogen atom and the molecule Hg—H. Since the energy required to dissociate hydrogen is 4.46 eV and the energy of the 6^3P_1 level of mercury is 4.85 eV, the excess internal energy amounts to 0.4 eV. The heat of dissociation of HgH molecules is comparable with 0.4 eV so the molecules must be vibrationally excited. Because of the weak Hg—H bond and the vibrational excitation in the molecule, the dissociation into Hg atoms and H atoms occurs most readily. Thus the *over-all reaction* is

$$Hg^*(6^3P_1) + H_2 \rightarrow Hg(6^1S_0) + 2H(1^2S_0)$$

It is worth noting that this over-all reaction does not specify the mechanism of the reaction. The reactions of excited mercury atoms with a host of molecules have been studied in great detail. Many of them ultimately give rise to chemical decomposition and the mechanism of the primary step is usually either photosensitization or hydrogen abstraction, as in the above reaction.

7–5 SUMMARY

1. Sensitized fluorescence involves the emission of light by a species that is indirectly excited by a nonradiative process during a collision with another electronically excited species. The experimental results indicate that gas kinetic energy can be utilized to complete the energy balance.

2. The inert gases have metastable states of extremely long mean lifetime. The term scheme for helium in Fig. 7–3 is particularly revealing. Notice that the energy scale is in wavenumbers and the S-P or S-P-D splittings are very small compared with the energy of the states. For example the $2S$–$2P$ separation is about 5000 cm^{-1} (0.63 eV) and the $3S$–$3P$–$3D$ separations are much less than this. The diagram also illustrated the Hund rule since ^3S always lies below ^1S, and ^3P and ^3D are below ^1P and ^1D, respectively. The S-P separations are greater for the triplets than the singlets. The 2^3S state of helium is so metastable that at one time it was thought that helium existed in two forms. These were called orthohelium (singlet) and parahelium (triplet). From the chemical point of view perhaps one of the most interesting aspects

of the state diagram is the immense energy gap between the ground and first excited state. This gap relates to the $1s \rightarrow 2s$ promotional energy. Since the helium electrons must undergo this promotion before they may participate in chemical bonds, it is not surprising that the atoms are inert. For argon the gap is about 11.5 eV, which is still an extremely large promotional energy. For xenon the $5p$–$6s$ promotional energy is about 8.5 eV, which is very nearly twice the $6s$–$6p$ separation for mercury. It should be reemphasized that the difference in energy between two configurations (orbitals) is not equal to the difference between two stationary states arising from these configurations, because the electron-electron interactions are not the same in each configuration. However, when the separations are large the state energies are a useful guide to the relative orbital energies.

3. The degree of interaction between atoms is dependent on the closeness of their energy states. Transfer of excitation energy between two atoms is most efficient when resonance conditions prevail. The mercury-sensitized fluorescence of sodium vapor is an experimental verification of this fact. The energy-transfer efficiency is sensitive to the energy gap for still another reason; the highest probability for electronic energy transfer occurs when the least amount of kinetic energy is created or employed during the process.

4. Nonradiative transitions between states in an atom can be induced by collision processes with other atoms or molecules. Molecules are usually more efficient than atoms in such collisions since the excess or defect of energy can be taken up as, or obtained from, the vibrational energy of the molecule. For example, nitrogen (N_2) is particularly effective in quenching mercury 2537-A resonance radiation. This is because N_2 has a vibrational state close in energy to the gap between the $^3P_1$ and $3P_0$ (metastable) states of mercury (see Fig. 6–3).

VIII

The Behavior of Atoms in Magnetic Fields

IT HAS LONG BEEN RECOGNIZED that the magnetic properties of materials are closely related to the electronic structures of the individual atoms. Of the three main types of magnetism—diamagnetism, paramagnetism, and ferromagnetism—only the last is a composite property of matter. Diamagnetism and paramagnetism are properties of individual atoms.

8-1 RELATION BETWEEN ELECTRIC CURRENT AND MAGNETIC FIELDS

Since the electrons in atoms are in continual motion, there is a magnetic field associated with this motion. The magnitude of the field depends on the total angular momentum of the electrons in the atom—that is, it depends on the quantum number J. If, for the present, we regard each atom as a small magnet, it is easy to visualize that there would be a force exerted on the atom by an external magnetic field. The total angular momentum J is a directional property and in the presence of a directing field the number of possible orientations of J with respect to the field direction are limited by quantum restrictions. The various possible orientations of J in a magnetic field are labeled by another quantum number, M_J, which is the magnetic-orientation quantum number. The student should compare this with m_L (Chap. V), which was the orientation quantum number for orbital angular momentum alone. The rules for obtaining the M_J values for a given J are the same as those used to obtain the m_L values for a given L, namely,

$$M_J = J, \quad J - 1, \quad J - 2, \ . \ . \ . \ 0, \ . \ . \ . \ , -J$$

Thus there are $(2J + 1)$ values of M_J for a given value of J. These different values of M_J are of course extant even in the absence of a magnetic field, but in that circumstance the M_J states are indistinguishable. In the absence of a field each J level is in reality $(2J + 1)$ states of equal energy. Since each value of M_J corresponds to a unique orientation of the total angular momentum J to the applied magnetic field, it is clear that each value of M corresponds to a different energy in the field. This is most readily understood if the M values are visualized as orientations of tiny bar magnets in a field; the force exerted on the magnet depends on its orientation in the field, hence the energy of interaction between the field and the magnet also depends on the orientation. At this point the student should refer to the discussion of space quantization in Chap. V. The permitted values of M_J are just the projections of J onto the direction of the field.

From the above discussion we are at once led to the conclusion that the single atomic levels of previous chapters, each characterized by a particular value of J, are split into $(2J + 1)$ **states** in the presence of a magnetic field. Experimental measurements of this splitting were first effected by Zeeman (1896), and the splitting of spectral lines in a magnetic field is called the **Zeeman effect.**

8–2 THE ZEEMAN EFFECT FOR SINGLET STATES

Each J level of the atom becomes $(2J + 1)$ closely spaced states in a magnetic field. The energy of the M_J state depends on the strength of the magnetic field and on the value of M_J. The separation between two successive M_J states is directly proportional to the field strength. Thus to each transition between electronic levels of different J there will correspond a set of transitions between states of different M_J in the presence of a field. A typical splitting pattern is shown in Fig. 8–1. On the left are shown the two levels ${}^1S_0$ and ${}^1P_1$, and the transition ${}^1S_0 \rightarrow {}^1P_1$ is detected as a single line in the absence of the field. When the magnetic field is switched on, the stationary states of the atom are no longer given by the number of values of J but by M_J, the orientations of J in the field. The ${}^1S_0$ level does not split since, for $J = 0$, M_J can have just the one value $M_J = J = 0$. For $J = 1$ the number of M_J values is

$$(2J + 1) = 3$$

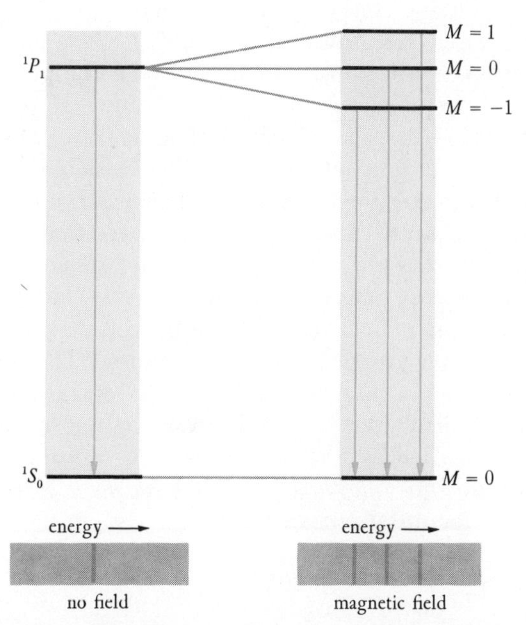

Figure 8–1 Zeeman effect for a ${}^1P_1 \rightarrow {}^1S_0$ transition. The Zeeman splitting is exaggerated in relation to the ${}^1P_1 \longleftrightarrow {}^1S_0$ separation.

and the possible values of M_J are 1, 0, and -1. Before we are able to predict the number of observed spectral lines, we must know the selection rules for changes in the quantum number M_J. These are similar to the rules for J;

$$\Delta M_J = 0, \pm 1$$

with the provision that transitions between $M_J = 0$ and $M'_J = 0$ are forbidden when $\Delta J = 0$.

In the present example $\Delta J = 1$, so transitions from the lower state $M_J = 0$ to each of the upper states $M'_J = 0, 1, -1$ are allowed. Thus the single line ${}^1S_0 \leftrightarrow {}^1P_1$ is split into three equally spaced lines in the presence of a field. Notice that the upper state with $M'_J = 0$ occurs at the same energy as the original line without the field. This is a manifestation of the fact that, when $M_J = 0$, J has no projection onto the field and hence this value of M corresponds to the state for which there is no interaction with the field. As a second example consider the transition ${}^1P_1 \leftrightarrow {}^1D_2$, which is allowed by the selection rules for S, L, and J. The magnetically unperturbed levels are shown in Fig. 8–2. In the presence of a magnetic field the ${}^1P_1$ level will split into three M_J states with $M_J = 1, 0,$ and -1. The ${}^1D_2$ level will split into $(2J + 1) = 5$ states with $M_J = 2, 1, 0, -1,$ and -2. The width of the multiplet of lines will be greater for the upper state since J, and hence the extent of interaction with the field, is larger for that level. The energy difference between successive M_J states *is not dependent on* J, so the same energy gaps occur for all states. The various possible transitions are indicated and it will be seen that they may be separated into three groups of isoenergetic lines. Thus only three equally spaced lines should be observed in the spectrum.

It is not difficult to extend these examples and make the following generalization: *Spectral lines due to transitions between singlet states are split into three lines by a magnetic field.* This is known as the **normal Zeeman effect.**

8–3 ZEEMAN SPLITTING AND THE GYROMAGNETIC RATIO OF ATOMS

The atom, like a classical magnetic bar, can have a magnetic moment. As was mentioned previously this magnetic moment

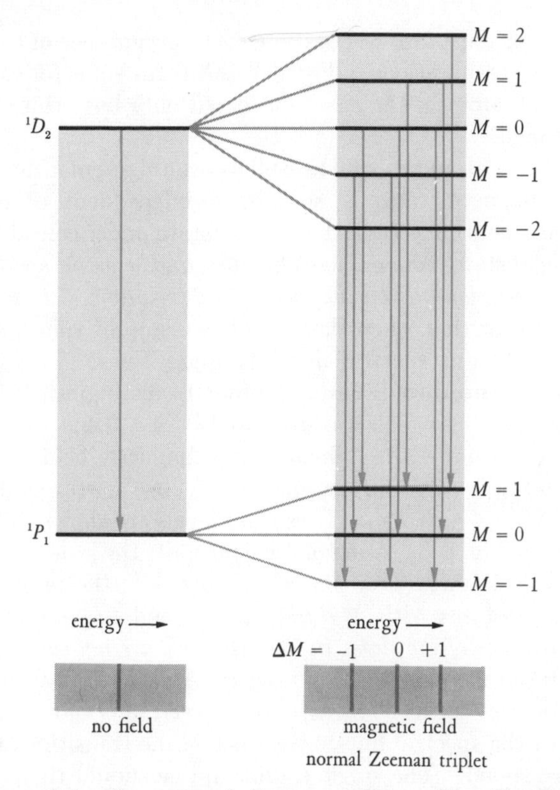

Figure 8–2 The normal Zeeman effect. The Zeeman splitting is exaggerated in relation to the $^1P_1 \longleftrightarrow {}^1D_2$ separation. The magnitude of the Zeeman splitting is proportional to the magnitude field strength.

must depend on the motion of electrons within the atom. A constant of the motion for electrons in a central field is angular momentum; the magnetic moment of the atom is proportional to the orbital angular momentum. Note that the proportionality only applies to the orbital angular momentum L. The ratio of the magnetic moment to L is called the **gyromagnetic ratio** for the atom, and this ratio is a constant for any kind of orbital motion. It is the gyromagnetic ratio that determines the spacing of energy levels in a magnetic field and, since this ratio is constant, the spacing of energy levels must also be constant. The acceptance of these facts justifies our assumptions in Fig. 8–2 (ΔE is the same for each level) because the atom in the case considered only has orbital angular momentum.

When an atom has spin as well as orbital angular momentum, the gyromagnetic ratio is no longer independent of the total angular momentum. Indeed when the state under consideration is not a singlet state, *the gyromagnetic ratio, and hence the spacing of the Zeeman levels, depends on the three quantum numbers L, S, J.* We shall see below that when the atom has resultant spin a magnetic field can split one spectral line into many lines. This has been called the **anomalous Zeeman effect** to distinguish it from the case where $S = 0$, which was discussed in Sec. 8–2.

Let us examine the influence of a magnetic field on the two sodium D-lines. The higher energy line (D_2) corresponds to the transition $3^2S_{1/2} \leftrightarrow 3^2P_{3/2}$. These two levels are shown on the left-hand side of Fig. 8–3. A magnetic field splits the ground state into $(2J + 1) = 2$ states with $M_J = +\frac{1}{2}$ and $-\frac{1}{2}$; the upper state is split into 4 states with $M_J = \frac{3}{2}, \frac{1}{2}, -\frac{1}{2}$ and $-\frac{3}{2}$. However *the energy spacings of the states in the two levels are not equal.* Within the limitations of the selection rules for M_J, the transitions shown in Fig. 8–3 can occur. The expected spectrum is shown schematically with the spectral lines drawn below the transitions to which they correspond. The single sodium D-line should therefore split into six components in the magnetic field. By similar reasoning, based on the previous discussion, we can deduce that the lines that are due to the $^2S_{1/2} \leftrightarrow {}^2P_{1/2}$ transition will split into four lines in a magnetic field. The actual emission spectrum of sodium in the region of the D lines is shown in Plate III. Notice that the Zeeman splitting is smaller than the spin-orbit interactions that separate the D lines. The splitting is usually of the order of a few reciprocal centimeters for normally obtainable magnetic fields. We cannot pursue the details of the relative intensities of the Zeeman components in this discussion, since this could not be done without recourse to the mathematical framework of quantum mechanics. The same comment is true of the relative values of the gyromagnetic ratio that determine the magnitude of the splitting for each state. Suffice it to say that the ratio varies by a factor of two over

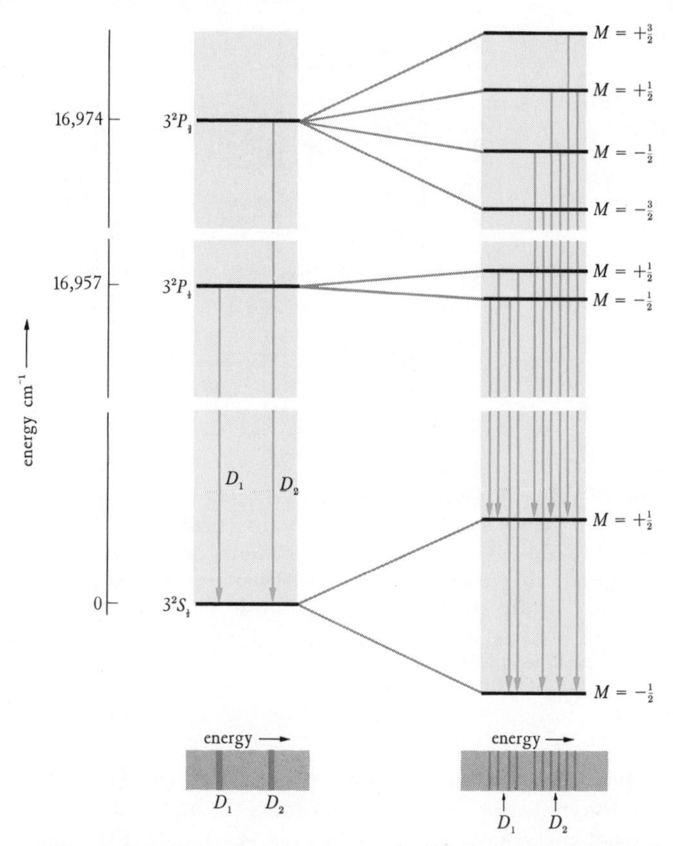

Figure 8–3 The origin of the anomalous Zeeman effect for the sodium-D lines. Note the breaks in the energy scale.

all possible values of L, S, and J (see Sec. 7–5). Although the Zeeman effect with spin is called anomalous, it is a much more common occurrence than the so-called normal Zeeman effect.

8–4 EXPERIMENTAL CONFIRMATION OF SPACE QUANTIZATION

An experiment by Stern and Gerlach (1924) proved unambiguously that the angular momentum of an atom is quantized in space.

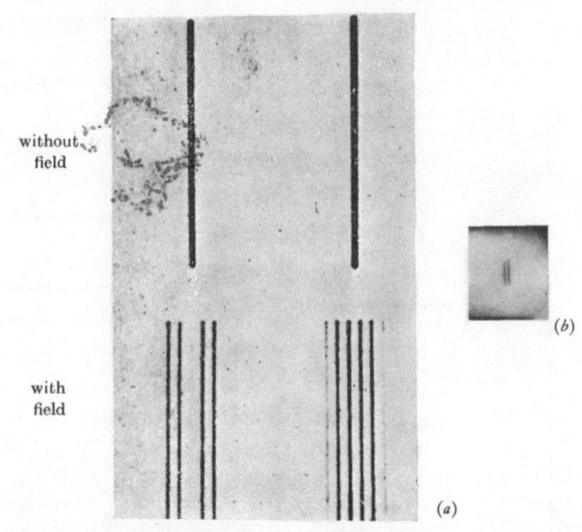

Plate III ***(a)*** **Anomalous Zeeman effect of Na $3^2S_{1/2}$ – $3^2P_{3/2}$; (5890 A) and $3^2S_{1/2}$ – $3^2P_{1/2}$ (5896 A). [From H. G. Kuhn, *Atomic Spectra*, Academic, New York, 1962, plate 8.]** ***(b)*** **Stern-Gerlach experiment results for potassium. [From A. C. Candler, *Atomic Spectra and the Vector Model*, Vol. I, Cambridge University Press, Cambridge, 1937, plate VI, 3.]**

The experimental arrangement is shown schematically in Fig. 8–4. The basic idea is to pass a beam of atoms through a magnetic field and onto a surface on which the spatial structure of the emergent atomic beam can be analyzed. The stream of atoms from a hot oven is collimated by the two slits S_1 and S_2 and condensed on the cold plate P, after passing through an inhomogeneous field pro-

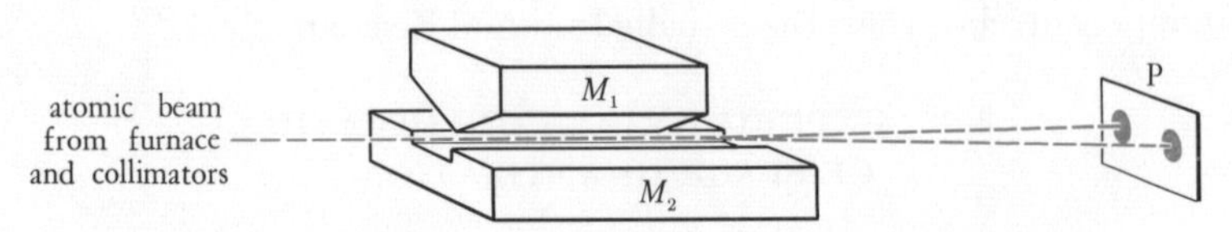

Figure 8–4 Schematic diagram of the Stern-Gerlach experiment.

vided by from the electromagnet with pole pieces M_1 and M_2. An inhomogeneous field is one for which the field strength varies from place to place. The greatest inhomogeneity of field is obtained when the variation of field strength per unit distance is greatest. An homogeneous field is one in which the field strength does not vary from point to point. When an atom with a magnetic moment (resultant angular momentum) is passed through an homogeneous field the magnetic moment interacts with the field. The resultant force tends to align the magnetic moment in the field direction. Some atoms align in one direction and some in other directions, depending on their original orientations as they entered the field. However, only one atomic beam will emerge from the field since *no force acts on the atoms that would cause them to travel at right angles to the direction of the field.* When an inhomogeneous field is employed, the atoms each experience a deflecting force resulting from the difference in the field strength at the two poles of the magnet. For this to occur appreciably it is necessary to have a field that is inhomogeneous even over extremely short distances (on the order of a few atomic diameters). In the actual experiment one pole piece M_1 was cut to a very sharp edge, while the other M_2 was cut as shown in Fig. 8–4. The field at the sharp edge of a pole piece such as M_1 is extremely large and falls off very rapidly with distance when placed at the groove of pole piece M_2.

This experiment has been performed for many atoms from which we shall choose three examples:

1. Zinc. Normal zinc atoms have the electronic configuration $[Ar]3d^{10}4s^2$, and thus the ground state is 4^1S_0. There should be one distinct orientation to the magnetic field since $(2J + 1) = (2 \times 0 + 1)$. The Stern-Gerlach experiment results in only *one sharp spot* on the condensing plate. The same results are obtained for cadmium, mercury, and the inert gases, all of which have $^1S_0$ ground states.

2. Sodium. The ground state of sodium is $3^2S_{1/2}$. In this case two sharp spots symmetrically placed about the central line are obtained on the plate. According to our previous discussions if $J = \frac{1}{2}$, $(2J + 1) = 2$; there should be precisely two possible orientations of the angular momentum with respect to the applied field. This experiment proves that the quantum restrictions on orientation are correct. The same result is obtained for the other alkali metals (see Plate III).

3. ***Oxygen.*** The ground state is 2^3P_2, and five spots are obtained in the experiment. One of the spots is located on the central line and corresponds to $M_J = 0$. The others are located symmetrically on either side of the center and correspond to the other allowed quantum orientations of J to the field, i.e., $M_J = -2$, -1, 1, 2.

It is also possible to measure the gyromagnetic ratio for atoms by this technique, since the ratio determines the extent of separation of the emerging beams. It is important for the student to understand that the atoms do not emerge from the furnace in a variety of M_J states that are ultimately separated by the field. The proper view is that atoms in the J level enter the field, which then only permits certain orientations of the angular momentum to persist.

The Zeeman splittings are of the order of a few reciprocal centimeters, so it is possible to induce transitions between the M_J states with electromagnetic radiation of the appropriate energy. The appropriate waves lie in the microwave range (radar frequencies) and the experimental arrangements are electrical instead of optical, although the principles of measurement are the same in each case. This branch of spectroscopy is called electron magnetic resonance.

Atomic spectral lines are also affected by electric fields, giving rise to the **Stark effect.** The Stark effect is more complex than the Zeeman effect because the term splitting in an electric field is not simply proportional to the field strength. Although the Stark effect has far-reaching consequences in molecular theory, it is of no particular value in analyses of atomic spectra.

8–5 SUMMARY

1. The magnitude of the magnetic moment associated with the motion of electrons in atoms depends on the total angular-momentum quantum number J; the total angular momentum for a given J is $\sqrt{J(J+1)}h/2\pi$.

The angular momentum is space quantized in the presence of a magnetic field; the number of orientations to the field is $(2J + 1)$.

3. Each atomic level of given J is split into $(2J + 1)$ states in a magnetic field. This is known as the Zeeman effect.

4. For states with no resultant spin the magnitude of the splitting between successive M_J states does not depend on the value of J. Thus only three spectral lines are observed in each Zeeman multiplet. This is known as the normal Zeeman effect.

5. (By way of an appendix) in general the separation between successive M states depends on the quantum numbers L, S, and J. For any kind of orbital motion the gyromagnetic ratio is a constant γ, which depends on the electronic change e, and mass m, as follows:

$$\gamma = \frac{e}{2mc}$$

The spacing of energy levels in a magnetic field of strength H is given by $H\gamma h/2\pi$. Thus the spacing ΔE_L for atoms with only orbital angular momentum is

$$\Delta E_L = \frac{Heh}{4\pi mc}$$

Notice that this expression is independent of J, which agrees with the assertion in paragraph 4 regarding the normal Zeeman effect. It is found that the spacings for states with orbital and spin momentum may be written

$$\Delta E_{LS} = g\Delta E_L$$

where g is known as the Landé splitting factor and is a function of L, S, and J.

$$g = 1 + \frac{J(J+1) + S(S+1) - L(L+1)}{2J(J+1)}$$

Note that the maximum and minimum values of g are 2 and 1, respectively. When $S = 0$ and $J = L$, then $g = 1$, which recovers the value for ΔE_L.

6. According to the last two expressions in paragraph 5, the energy spacings are functions of L, S, and J and thus vary from state to state. Consequently more than three lines can be ob-

served in the Zeeman pattern. This is called the anomalous Zeeman effect.

7. The Stern-Gerlach experiment proves that the total angular momentum of the atom is space-quantized in a magnetic field. The number of orientations of J to the field is shown experimentally to be $2J + 1$.

8. We can always associate the M_J values with the projections of the total angular momentum onto a fixed reference axis, namely, the direction of the magnetic field. Although the M_J values are rational numbers, the total angular momentum is $J^* = \sqrt{J(J+1)}$; therefore the direction of J^* can *never* be precisely along the direction of the field. When J is very large, J^* is *nearly* equal to J (a rational number), and now the total angular momentum can be *nearly* along the field direction in two of the states. Of course when J is very large the system becomes less clearly quantized (correspondence principle) and concomitantly the distinction between levels and states becomes less clear.

IX

Some of the Forces between Atoms: The Simplest Molecules

In previous chapters we have been principally concerned with the properties of individual atoms. During the discussions on sensitized fluorescence, collisional deactivation, and excimer formation, we did not consider the details of the interactions between the atomic species in the systems. By way of a prelude to the reader's ultimate interest in molecules, we shall end with a few brief discussions on weak atom-atom interactions. Discussion of normal covalent bonding is not appropriate to this monograph.

9–1 VAN DER WAALS INTERACTION

When two neutral, ground-state neon atoms approach there is a very slight attractive force. The electrons in one atom are weakly attracted to the nucleus of the other atom. The extent of the stabilization is small compared with the average kinetic energy of the particles, so in a gas at normal temperature and pressure Ne_2

molecules would not be easily detectable. Weak interactions of this type are known as **van der Waals interactions.** An approximate magnitude of the energy of van der Waals bonds can be gleaned from the heats of sublimation of molecular crystals. The heat of sublimation of neon is about 475 cal/g-atom, which corresponds to 2.04×10^{-2} eV. The energy of interaction between neon atoms has this order of magnitude, whereas the mean kinetic energy in a gas at 300°K is 900 cal/g-atom (cf. Sec. 7–3). The potential-energy curve for the approach of two neon atoms will resemble the lower curve in Fig. 9–1.

We expect a different interaction between an excited and unexcited neon atom. In order to see this more clearly, we shall rescrutinize the nature of van der Waals forces. An atom is electrically neutral and its charge distribution is spherically symmetrical. Thus the atom has no electric dipole moment—the centers of charge and mass are coincident. It is useful to consider that the atom has fluctuating electric dipoles that, within the time scale of an experiment, average out to zero. Thus, for very short periods of time the electron density can be larger on one side of the atom than on the other. When these classical concepts are translated into the language of quantum mechanics we can determine that there is a net force between neutral atoms that corresponds to the interaction between the two fluctuating electric dipoles. This is what we have previously called a van der Waals force.

9–2 RESONANCE COUPLING

When the atom interacts with electromagnetic radiation there is once again a dipole-dipole interaction between the fluctuating charge distribution of the atom and the oscillating electric dipole of the radiation. During the process of electronic excitation, the atom develops a dipole that could be regarded as oscillating at the frequency of the electromagnetic wave. This oscillating dipole is usually called a **transition moment dipole.** As before, this discussion is not intended to infer that the atom acquires a permanent dipole moment after the optical excitation. The transition dipole of one atom may interact with the electrons of a nearby ground-

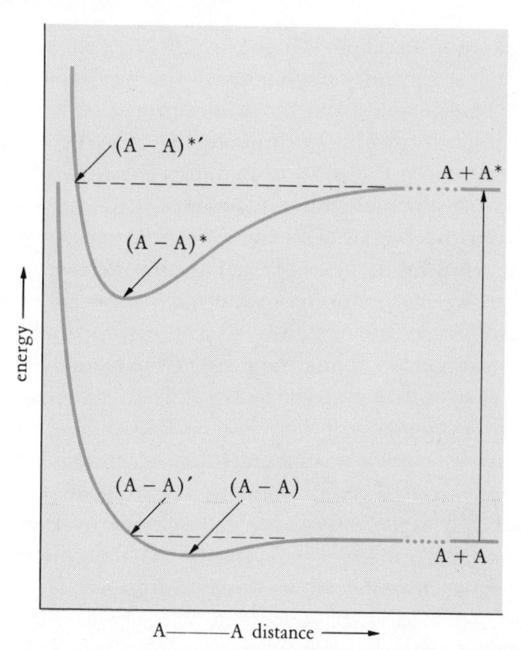

Figure 9–1 The potential curves for the interaction between ground-state *A* atoms (lower curve) and an excited state with a ground-state atom (upper curve). (*A* − *A*) represents the weakly bonded ground-state molecule and (*A* − *A*)′ is this molecule with just sufficient vibrational energy for dissociation. (*A* − *A*)* is the electronically excited diatomic molecule and (*A* − *A*)*′ represents the excited molecule with vibrational energy.

state atom. The result of this interaction is to cause the excitation energy to be transferred from one atom to the other. In effect, the system of two separate atoms becomes one system of two atoms. One of the pair is excited but the probability of a particular one being in the excited state is only 50 per cent. We cannot distinguish between $Ne_{(1)}^* Ne_{(2)}$ and $Ne_{(1)} Ne_{(2)}^*$.

If we regarded the excitation as building up in atom (1) as it decays in atom (2), we would obtain an approximate idea of the interaction between the two atoms by considering the energy of two electric dipoles placed apart at the apropriate distance. This type of interaction is formally analogous to the mechanical coupling of two pendula suspended from the same support. The motion of the first pendulum is gradually imitated by the other which subsequently reinduces the motion in the original pendulum, and so on. This is the phenomenon of resonance, which arises in classical and quantum mechanics whenever the interacting systems have the same natural frequencies of oscillation. *Resonance coupling as described here normally applies to systems that are very much isolated from one another*, so that virtually no interaction would occur in the absence of resonance. Thus the present model should not be seriously carried over into systems of strongly coupled oscillators such as π-electron systems.

We can assume a resonance-force interaction between the excited and unexcited neon atoms in the experiment of Sec. 7–4; this interaction is less sensitive to changes in the interatomic distance than the van der Waals forces. If we limit the resonance to dipole-dipole interactions as described above, the stabilization energy turns out to be proportional to r^{-3}, whereas the van der Waals energies are proportional to r^{-6}.

The characteristic potential curve for resonance interaction of two atoms is shown in the upper part of Fig. 9–1. At large values of r the interaction is vanishingly small and the position on the energy scale corresponds to the excitation of a single atom. At extremely short internuclear distances the repulsive forces predominate. Thus there is a deep minimum of energy corresponding to the molecule (A-A)*. If there are sufficient atoms in the system to permit a number of exchanges of kinetic energy, the vibrating (A-A)* can be stabilized and exist until such time as it emits a quantum of radiation. If the pressure of the gas is low, making the cross section for kinetic-energy exchange low, the molecule may fly apart before it can radiate. These reactions are described by the following equations:

$$\begin{array}{ccccc} A^* + A & \rightleftharpoons & A_2^{*\prime} & \xrightleftharpoons{\text{collisions}} & A_2^* \rightarrow h\nu + 2A \\ & & \downarrow & & \\ & & 2A + h\nu & & \end{array}$$

Note that after radiating the species is no longer diatomic since, as we have already seen, there is negligible association of the atoms in the ground state. The prime indicates that the molecule has sufficient vibrational energy to spontaneously dissociate.

9–3 VIBRATIONAL STATES

We are still faced with the question of explaining the emission process for the excited diatomic molecule Ne_2^*. Before arriving at the answer to this question we must first examine the detailed motions of the nuclei after the association of the two atoms. The molecule may be stabilized by losing kinetic energy during collisions, but it cannot lose an arbitrary amount of kinetic energy. The internuclear motions, like the electronic motions, are quantized, and the molecule has a definite set of discrete vibrational states. Each vibrational state approximately corresponds to a multiple of the natural vibrational frequency of the molecule. Two masses that are constrained to move relative to one another under the influence of a force proportional to their distance apart, are classically bound to oscillate at a definite frequency that depends only on the masses of the particles and the magnitude of the restoring force. This frequency is the natural frequency of the system. Quantum mechanically the system has a set of vibrational states that are separated by energies corresponding to integral multiples of the classical vibrational frequency. The energy of the nth vibrational state is

$$E_n = (n + \tfrac{1}{2})\bar{\nu} \text{ cm}^{-1} \qquad (9\text{–}1)$$

where $\bar{\nu}$ is the wavenumber of the natural frequency of oscillation of the nuclei. To this approximation the vibrational states are equally spaced, the energy spacing being ν,

$$E_n - E_{n-1} = (n + \tfrac{1}{2})\bar{\nu} - [(n - 1) + \tfrac{1}{2}]\bar{\nu}$$

Therefore

$$\Delta E = \bar{\nu}$$

These vibrational states are depicted in Fig. 9–2 as equally spaced horizontal lines within the electronic potential curve of the diatomic molecule. The vibrational spacings are on the order of

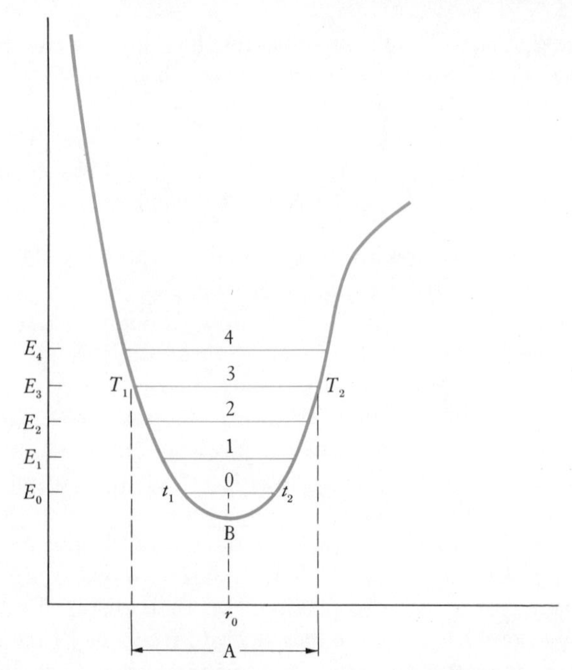

Figure 9–2 The vibrational states of a diatomic molecule.

one-tenth to one-hundredth of the energies of electronic states. While the molecule is in the vibrational state E_3 the nuclei can be regarded as undergoing a vibration of amplitude A. At the points T_1 and T_2 (turning points) the nuclei are at the extremities of the vibration, and they have only potential energy. During the pathway T_1BT_2 the nuclei first lose potential energy. After B the gain in kinetic energy is just sufficient to enable the point T_2 to be reached. The equilibrium internuclear separation r_0 corresponds to the center of the zero-point oscillation. This motion is not analogous to a classical vibration; otherwise there would be two most likely configurations for the molecule at the turning points t_1 and t_2! In the other vibrational states the motion is more classical and the nuclei spend most time in the neighborhood of the turning points.

This type of energy curve is a characteristic of all diatomic molecules.

In refinement certain aspects of the above discussion should be modified. For example, the energy spacings are not exactly equal because the nuclear motion is anharmonic; the nuclear motion is not classical but quantum mechanical, thus we can only measure the probability of the occurrence of certain internuclear separations; the vibrational and electronic parts of the system are not necessarily independent motions, as we have assumed.

Franck-Condon Principle

The **Franck-Condon principle** asserts that the internuclear distance does not change during a transition between two electronic states of a molecule. The nuclear motion is very slow compared with the electronic motions that take place when the molecule interacts with electromagnetic radiation. This condition appreciably simplifies the spectra of diatomic molecules, since it permits us to regard electronic transitions as vertical jumps between potential-energy curves. Electronic transitions that occur with no change in internuclear separation are known as **vertical transitions.** To a certain degree the Franck-Condon principle determines the relative intensity of vibrational bands in an electronic spectrum. The two potential curves in Fig. 9–3 represent the ground (S_0) and excited (S_1) states of a diatomic molecule. The transition $S_1 \rightarrow S_0$ is not characterized by a single line in the spectrum like an atomic transition. Suppose the excited S_1 molecules are each in zero-point vibrational levels; the most probable internuclear distance is r_1. According to the Franck-Condon principle the most probable transition occurs to the second vibrational level of the ground state. The resulting spectrum (neglecting rotation of the molecule) is shown schematically at the side of Fig. 9–3. The student should recall that the most probable transitions will be to molecules that have r values corresponding to turning points of the vibrations. After the electronic quantum jump, the molecule starts a vibrational motion corresponding to the classical route T_1AT_2.

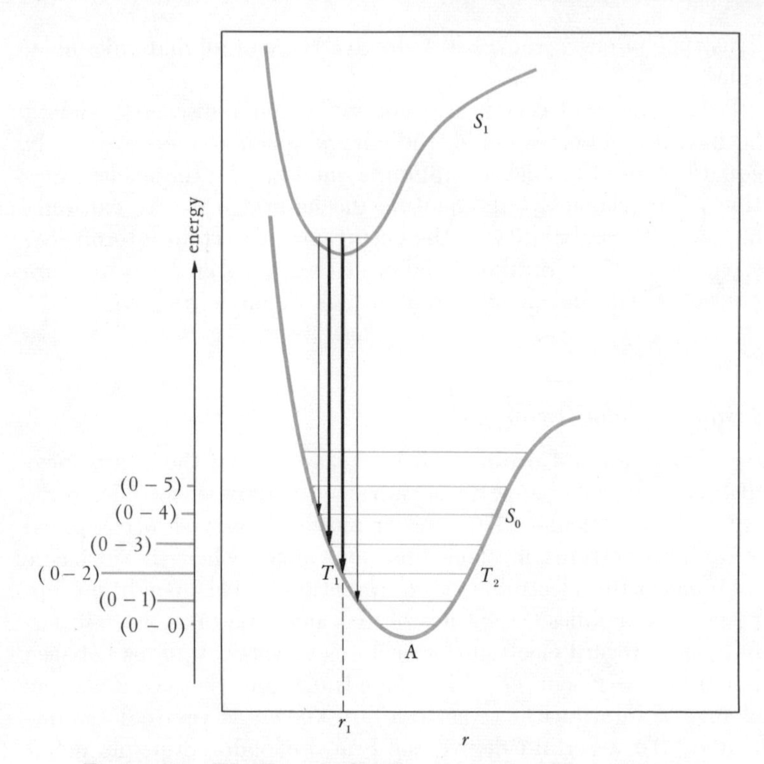

Figure 9–3 The Franck-Condon principle. The spectrum resulting from the transition $S_1 \rightarrow S_0$ is shown on the left-hand side; note that the transition 0–2 (i.e., zero-point vibration in the upper state to 2-vibrational quanta excited in the ground state) is the most intense.

Continuous Emission Spectra

We can now examine the emission of Ne_2* in greater detail. The potential curves for the ground and excited states are shown in Fig. 9–4. We shall suppose that the excited molecules are each in zero-point vibrational levels and that vertical transitions are the most probable (i.e., the most intense).

The ground-state stabilization energy is extremely small so

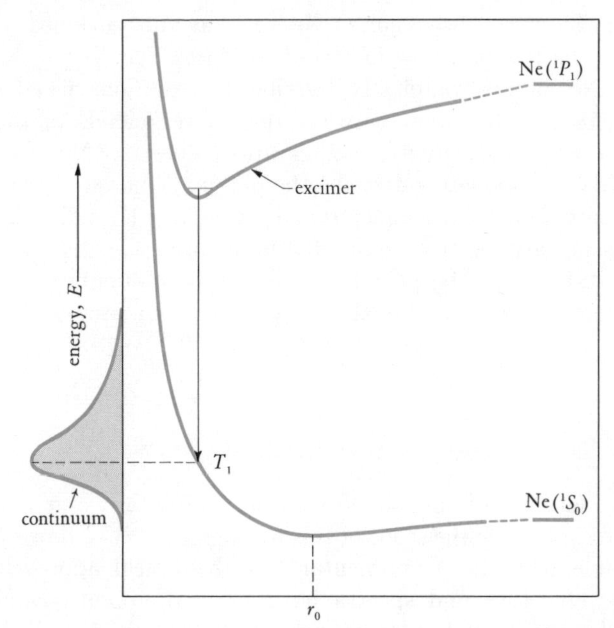

Figure 9–4 The origin of the rare-gas continuous spectrum.

there can be no quantization of vibration in the ground state. Classically this arises when the potential energy of the contracted nuclei at a turning point is greater than the energy required to dissociate the molecule. In other words the molecule is not able to undergo a complete vibrational cycle before it dissociates. In Fig. 9–4 the potential energy at T_1 is such that the kinetic energy developed after expansion to r_0 is sufficient to cause the molecule to dissociate. The emission spectrum does not consist of discrete vibrational lines but is instead continuous, corresponding to the production of two ground-state neon atoms with a continuous range of kinetic energies. The spectrum is shown on the left-hand side of the diagram with its maximum at the energy of the vertical transition.

In the above discussion of Ne_2^* we have not specified the nature of the bonding. In fact configurations like $Ne^* — Ne$ and $Ne — Ne^*$ do not completely describe the situation, since there is considerable interaction between the charge clouds of the two neon atoms. Accordingly, configurations like Ne^+Ne^- must be included to completely describe the bonding. Indeed the bonding is not different in principle from that in the H_2 molecule. The interesting aspect of rare-gas diatomic species is that they are quite stable once the pair of atoms has been supplied with the enormous $s — p$ promotional energy of one neon atour.

9–4 ATOMS IN MOLECULES

A detailed discussion of molecular structure and covalent bonding is outside the scope of this monograph. It is, however, remarkable how the experimental and theoretical approaches to atomic structure and spectra have in more recent years been carried over into molecular and solid-state studies. Franck-Hertz-type experiments have yielded important information about certain molecules; the Pauli principle is used to build up the electronic structure of molecules; molecules absorb and emit radiation according to selection rules that are formally analogous to the rules for atoms; long-range energy transfer between molecules is now a well-authenticated phenomenon; and the concept of atomic orbitals that describe the wave-characteristics of electrons in atoms can be extended to a molecular orbital description of the wave characteristics of electrons in molecules.

Suggested Readings

Max Born, *Atomic Physics*, Blackie, Edinburg, 1944.

H. S. Taylor and S. Glasstone, *Treatise on Physical Chemistry*, vol. I, *Atomistics and Thermodynamics*, Van Nostrand, Princeton, N.J., 1942.

G. Herzberg, *Atomic Spectra and Atomic Structure*, Dover, New York, 1944.

H. G. Kuhn, *Atomic Spectra*, Longmans, London, 1962.

P. Pringsheim, *Fluorescence and Phosphorescence*, Wiley-Interscience, New York, 1949.

J. C. Slater, *Introduction to Chemical Physics*, McGraw-Hill, New York, 1939.

W. J. Moore, *Physical Chemistry*, 3d ed., Prentice-Hall, Englewood Cliffs, N.J., 1962.

W. Heitler, *Wave Mechanics*, 2d ed., Oxford University Press, Oxford, 1956.

J. W. Linnet, *Wave Mechanics and Valency*, Wiley, New York, 1960.

G. M. Barrow, *The Structure of Molecules*, Benjamin, New York, 1963.

Suggested Readings

Index

Absorption spectrum, of mercury vapor, 10
of sodium vapor, 10
triplet-triplet, 121
Alkali metals, atomic beam experiments with, 142
spectra of, 85
screening effects in, 85
Alkaline earths, spectra of, 88
Amplitude, of waves, 4
of vibrations, 150
Angstrom, definition, 6
Angular distributions, 51
Angular momentum, addition of spin and orbital, 88
in alkaline earths, 88
definition, 37
and spatial orientation, 38
for spin, 55
Anomalous Zeeman effect, 138
Argon, energy levels of, 121
metastability of lowest triplet, 121
Atomic beam, in Stern-Gerlach experiment, 139
Atomic number, 65
Atomic orbitals, 48
Atomic radii, of alkali metals, 73
effect of screening on, 74

Balmer's formula, 12
Balmer series, fine structure of, 82
of hydrogen, 15
in stellar spectra, 32
Bohr postulate, wave-mechanical justification, 46
Bohr radius, unit, 41
theory of H, 14
Bohr theory, de Broglie waves in, 45
postulates, 22
in relation to uncertainty, 39
Boltzman constant, value of, 107
Boundary surfaces, of hydrogenic orbitals, 51

Cadmium, atomic beam experiment with, 141
Carbon, terms and levels of, 92
Central field, 38

Charge cloud, 42
Classical collisions, physical theory of, 106
Collision, atom-electron, 25
  of excited atoms with molecules, 129
Collision number, from classical theory, 107
Collisional deactivation, in sodium, 127
Combination principle, 23
  and wave mechanics, 44
Configurations, 57
  of electrons in atoms, 48
  formal definition, 78
Correspondence principle, 23
Coulomb's law, physical interpretation, 63
Critical excitation potentials, 28
Cross section, for atomic collisions, 115
  definition, 115
  for energy transfer, 120
  for kinetic-energy exchange, 148

Davisson and Germer experiment, 40
de Broglie principle, 43, 40
  waves in Bohr orbits, 45
Decay law, derivation, 112
Diamagnetism, 133
Diffraction, distinction from interference, 37
  of electrons from nickel, 40
  grating, 37
  patterns, 35
Dipole-dipole interaction, 96
  between atoms, 146
Dissociation of diatomic molecule, 153
Doublet, structure of H spectra, 84

Effective cross section, 117
Elastic collision, 21
Electric dipole moment, definition, 146
Electron, charge on, 2
Electron magnetic resonance, 142
Electron volts, conversion to cm $^{-1}$, 34
  definition, 34
Elliptic orbits, 45
Emission, continuous, 152
Energy levels, in magnetic field, 143
  spacing of, 143
Energy-transfer, cross section for, 116
  effect of near resonance on, 124
  efficiency of, 124
  between identical atoms, 123
  from mercury to sodium, 124
Equivalent orbitals, terms arising from, 93
Excimers, 129

Ferromagnetism, 133
Filled shell, stability of, 69
Filled subshell, stability of, 69
Flash spectroscopy, 128
Forbidden transitions, 102
Franck-Condon principle, in molecular spectra, 151
Franck-Hertz experiment, with mercury, 26
Frequency, definition, 4

Gyromagnetic ratio, formal definition, 143

measurement of, 142
for orbital motion, 137
for spinning electron, 138

Half-filled subshells, stability of, 70
Half-lifetime, 101
Heat of dissociation, of mercury hydride, 131
Helium, electronic states of, 121
ionization potential, 69
Helium discharge, singlet and triplet states, 121
Hund's rule, 63, 94
and Pauli principle, 69
physical interpretation, 63
Hydrogen, atomic spectrum of, 12
general formula for spectral lines of, 13
ionization potential, 69
Hydrogen abstraction, by mercury 131

Inelastic collision, 21
Inert gases, 141
metastable states of the, 131
resonance levels of the, 121
Intensity, relation to probability, 100
Interference, 36
Internuclear motions, quantization of, 149
Ionic radii, 75
Ionization continuum, 24
Ionization potential, definition, 21
effect of orbital structure on, 71
effect of screening on, 68
by electron impact, 32
of first row atoms, 71
Isolectronic, ions, 75

jj coupling, 95

Kinetic energy, 34
conversion to electronic energy in atom collisions, 120
definition, 20
in energy transfer processes, 119
transformation into potential energy, 21
Kinetic theory of gases, assumptions involved in, 107
effective cross section, 116

Landé splitting factor, formal definition, 143
Level, formal definition of, 79
symbol, 80
of various hydrogen configurations, 82
Lifetime, 100
Line spectra, 9
Lithium, ionization potential in relation to H and He, 69
Lyman series, fine structure of, 84
of hydrogen, 15, 31
series limit of, 31

Magnetic field, homogeneous and inhomogeneous, 140
splitting of $^1P_1$ level in, 136
Magnetic moment, 95
of the atom, 136
interaction between spin and orbital, 96
Many-electron atoms, orbital sequences, 65
Mean lifetime, 101
and collision frequency, 108
definition, 99

Measurement, statistical interpretation of, 41
Mechanical coupling, 148
Mercury, atomic beam experiment with, 141
  electronic states of, 30
  energy transfer to thallium, 117
  excitation potential of, 25
  reaction with hydrogen, 130
Metastable excited states and collision frequency, 108
Metastable state, absorption by, 128
  detected by electron collision, 28
  of mercury, 104
Multiplet, for hydrogen, 82
  in Zeeman effect, 136
Multiplicity, of levels, 79
  of spin, 81
  of terms, 79

Neon, interatomic interactions, 145
Nonradiative transitions between sodium levels, 127
Normal Zeeman effect, 136

Orbitals, *d*-type, 50
  hydrogen-like in complex atoms, 65
  p-type, 50, 57
Orthohelium, 131
Oxygen, 142

Pairing, of electrons in orbitals, 58
Parahelium, 131
Paramagnetism, 133
Pauli exclusion principle, 58, 93
Pauli principle, and electron repulsion, 69
  and periodicity, 65
Period, definition, 4
Periodic table, 65
  classical trends in, 72
  electron configurations in, 71
Photocurrent, 19
Photoionization, 22
  of cesium, 129
  of hydrogen, 32
Photons, definition, 6
Photothreshold, 20
Planck's constant, 6
Planck's equation, 6
Positive ions, electronic configurations of, 75
Potassium, electron configuration, 67
Potential energy, of electrons in field, 20
  of two neon atoms, 146
Probability, in measurements, 41
  of radiative transition, 99
Probability distributions, for 3*d* and 4*s* orbitals, 67
Promotional energy, and chemical reactivity, 132

Quantum number, M_J, 134
  magnetic, 49
  for orbital angular momentum, 45
  principal, 44
  for total angular momentum J, 134

Radial density, 53
Radial distributions, 51, 52

Radial probability, distribution curve, 41
Rare gases, ionization potentials, 70
Rate constant, relation to lifetime, 113
Refractive index, 5
Repulsion, physical description, 92
Repulsion energies, for electrons, 63
Resonance, 122, 146
Resonance fluorescence, 12
Resonance force, between neon atoms, 148
Resonance levels, of alkaline earths, 106
Resonance lines, 12
Russell-Saunders coupling, 95
Rydberg constant, 12
Rydberg formula, 15

Screening, 64
Selection rules, approximations in, 102
  for changes in M_J, 136
  effect of spin-orbital coupling on, 96
  for J, 82
  for $J = 0 \rightarrow J = 0$, 104
  for L, 84
  for spin, 91
  violation of, by collisions, 127
Sensitized fluorescence, definition, 117
Shells, effect on valence electrons, 66
  filled, 66
  structure of atoms, 44
Shielding, of mercury valence electrons, 104
Singlet terms, of alkaline earths, 89
Sodium, 141
  absorption spectrum of, 87
  D-lines, 88, 127
  energy levels, 126
  Zeeman effect on, 138
Space quantization, 134
  experimental confirmation of, 139
Spatial degeneracy, 64
Spectral lines, emission after electron collision, 28
Spin, of electron, 54
Spin-orbital coupling, comparison with Zeeman splittings, 138
  dependence on Z, 103
  energy of, 96
  physical description, 95
Spin-orbital splitting, in alkali metals, 88
  doublet structure form, 88
Stark effect, use of, 142
States, formal definition, 79
  stationary, 22
Steady state, definition, 110
  in photochemistry, 109
Stern and Gerlach experiment, 139
Subshells, arrangement of electrons in, 60
  filled and half-filled, 68

Terms, formal definition, 79
  symbol, 80
Thallium, energy levels of, 118
  sensitized fluorescence by mercury, 117
Total-binding energy, effect of electron repulsion on, 69
Transition-metal ions, electronic configuration of, 75
Transition-moment dipole, 146
Triplet terms, of alkaline earths, 89
Turning points, of vibrations, 150

Uncertainty principle, 41

Vacuum wavelengths, 6
van der Waals interactions, magnitude, 146
Vector method, for carbon p^2, 92
  for coupling L and S, 91
Vertical transitions, in diatomic molecules, 151
Vibrational energy, in neon excimers, 149
Vibrational frequency, of diatomic molecule, 149
Vibrational state, of diatomic molecules, 149
  energy expression for, 149
  spacing of, 149

Wave, 4
  amplitude, 4
  equation, 43
  and wave function, 48
Wavelength, definition, 4
Wavenumber, 7
Work function, equation for metal, 33
  of metal, 20

Zeeman effect, 134
  for singlet states, 134
Zeeman levels, dependence on L, S, and J, 138
Zeeman splitting, comparison with spin-orbit, 138
Zero energy, definition, 61
Zero-point vibration, 153
Zinc, 141